D1404974

FAO-Unesco
Soil map of the world
1 : 5 000 000
Volume III
Mexico and Central America

FAO-Unesco

Soil map of the world

FOOD AND AGRICULTURE ORGANIZATION OF THE UNITED NATIONS

UNITED NATIONS EDUCATIONAL, SCIENTIFIC AND CULTURAL ORGANIZATION

FAO - Unesco

Soil map of the world

1 : 5 000 000

Volume III

Mexico and Central America

Prepared by the Food and Agriculture Organization
of the United Nations

Unesco - Paris 1975

Printed by Tipolitografia F. Failli, Rome
for the Food and Agriculture Organization of the
United Nations
and the United Nations Educational, Scientific and
Cultural Organization

Published in 1975 by the United Nations Educational,
Scientific and Cultural Organization
Place de Fontenoy, 75700 Paris

ISBN 92 - 3 - 101127 - 8

The project for a joint FAO/Unesco Soil Map of the World was undertaken following a recommendation of the International Society of Soil Science. It is the first attempt to prepare, on the basis of international cooperation, a soil map covering all the continents of the world in a uniform legend, thus enabling the correlation of soil units and comparisons on a global scale. The project, which started in 1961, fills a gap in present knowledge of soil potentialities throughout the world and provides a useful instrument in planning agricultural and economic development programmes.

The project has been carried out under the scientific authority of an international advisory panel, within the framework of FAO and Unesco programmes. The different stages of the work included comparative studies of soil maps, field and laboratory work, and the organization of international expert meetings and study tours. The secretariat of the joint project, located at FAO headquarters, was vested with the responsibility of compiling the technical information, correlating the studies and drafting the maps and text. FAO and Unesco shared the expenses involved in the realization of the project, and Unesco undertook publication of its results. For the preparation of the Soil Map of Mexico and Central America, the services of associate experts were made available by the Governments of Belgium and the Netherlands to work on the project.

The present volume, covering the soils of Mexico, Central America and the Caribbean islands, is the third of a set of ten which make up the complete publication of the Soil Map of the World. The first volume records introductory information and presents the definitions of the elements of the legend which is used uniformly throughout the publication. Each of the nine following volumes comprises an explanatory text and the corresponding map sheets covering the main regions of the world.

FAO and Unesco wish to express their gratitude to the government institutions, the International Society of Soil Science, and the many individual soil scientists who have contributed so much to this international project.

CONTENTS

This volume describes the Mexican and Central American section of the 1 : 5 000 000 Soil Map of the World. The compilation of the Soil Map of Mexico and Central America was completed by FAO and Unesco in a joint project initiated in 1961.

The map

The map sheet which makes up the Soil Map of Mexico and Central America is drawn on topographic base maps of the 1 : 5 000 000 series of the American Geographical Society. The map units are associations of soil units divided into texture and slope classes. They are marked on the map by symbols. The dominant soils are shown by colours while phase differences are shown by overprints.

A small inset map shows three grades of reliability of soil information from which the map was compiled (Figure 1).

Detailed definitions of the soil units and full descriptions of all the terms used may be found in Volume I of the set.

The text

The first chapter describes the development of the project in Mexico and Central America and gives some notes on uses of the map. The second acknowledges the cooperation of the agencies and of the large number of people who contributed to the maps and text, and the third gives a summary of the material in Volume I on the maps and legend.

The principal chapters of this volume deal with environmental conditions, soils, and land use and soil suitability.

ENVIRONMENTAL CONDITIONS

Chapter 4 contains brief accounts, with maps, of the four factors of the environment that have close relationships with the pattern of soils: climate, vegetation, geology, and physiography and lithology.

Climate is discussed on the basis of six broad climatic subdivisions. Since the criteria used in delimiting units are those that are important to crop growth, the climatic map is supplementary to the soil map in the transfer of crop information from one part of the world to another. Here only the higher categories are discussed. The main climatic regions are outlined on a small-scale map (Figure 2).

Vegetation is discussed on the basis of 15 broad regions, which are outlined on a small-scale map (Figure 3). The text gives some brief notes on the ecological conditions, main plant species and distribution of the vegetation regions.

Geology, physiography and lithology are discussed in relation to major land forms. Physiography (Figure 4) and lithology (Figure 5) are also dealt with in relation to the nature and distribution of soil parent materials.

SOILS AND LAND USE

Chapter 5, describing the soils of Mexico and Central America, contains an extensive table of soil associations and an account of the distribution of the main soils. Chapter 6 discusses land use and soil suitabilities for agriculture.

The table of *soil associations* lists all the map units in alphabetical order of symbols. Other columns show:

Associated soils
Inclusions
Phases
Areas of units in 1 000 hectares
Countries of occurrence

The *distribution of major soils* is discussed on the basis of three broad soil regions — the continental highlands and lowlands, and the Caribbean islands — and outlined on a small-scale map (Figure 6). The main soils of each region are discussed in relation to factors of the environment, and their important characteristics are noted.

Present land use and suitability for agriculture are discussed, with an account of traditional and modern farming systems. Then the main soils are considered separately, with a description of their present use and the suitability of the land for both traditional and modern farming.

Le présent volume décrit la section Mexique et Amérique centrale de la Carte mondiale des sols au 1 : 5 000 000. La Carte des sols du Mexique et de l'Amérique centrale a été réalisée par la FAO et l'Unesco, dans le cadre d'un projet conjoint lancé en 1961.

La carte

La feuille cartographique qui constitue la Carte des sols du Mexique et de l'Amérique centrale a été établie d'après les fonds topographiques au 1 : 5 000 000 de l'American Geographical Society. Les unités cartographiques sont des associations d'unités pédologiques subdivisées selon les classes de texture et de pente. Elles sont indiquées sur la carte par des symboles. Les sols dominants sont représentés par des couleurs, tandis que les phases sont indiquées en surcharge.

Une carte à petite échelle reproduite en cartouche indique trois degrés de fiabilité des données pédologiques d'après lesquelles la carte a été établie (figure 1).

Des définitions détaillées des unités pédologiques et des descriptions complètes de tous les termes employés figurent dans le volume I de cette série.

Le texte

Le premier chapitre fait l'historique du projet au Mexique et en Amérique centrale, et donne quelques indications sur les utilisations possibles de la carte. Le deuxième chapitre rend hommage aux institutions et à ceux qui ont collaboré à la préparation des cartes et du texte, tandis que le troisième résume le contenu du volume I en ce qui concerne les cartes et la légende.

Le principaux chapitres de ce volume traitent du milieu, de la répartition, de l'utilisation et de la vocation des sols.

LE MILIEU

Le chapitre 4 traite brièvement, à l'aide de cartes, des quatre facteurs du milieu dont dépend étroitement la répartition des sols: climat, végétation, géologie, et physiographie et lithologie.

Le *climat* est traité sur la base de six grandes subdivisions climatiques. Etant donné que pour délimiter ces unités on a retenu les critères les plus importants pour la croissance des plantes, la carte climatique complète la carte des sols et doit être consultée pour le transfert des données sur les cultures d'une partie du monde à une autre. Il n'est tenu compte ici que des catégories supérieures. Les principales zones climatiques sont délimitées sur la carte à petite échelle (figure 2).

L'étude de la *végétation* est basée sur 15 grandes régions qui sont représentées sur une carte à petite échelle (figure 3). Le texte donne quelques brèves indications sur les conditions écologiques, les espèces culturales les plus importantes et la répartition des régions selon la végétation.

La *géologie*, la *physiographie* et la *lithologie* ont été étudiées par rapport aux principales formes de relief. La physiographie (figure 4) et la lithologie (figure 5) ont également été traitées d'après la nature et la distribution des matériaux originels des sols.

SOLS ET UTILISATION DES TERRES

Le chapitre 5, qui décrit les sols du Mexique et de l'Amérique centrale, contient un tableau détaillé des associations de sols et une description de la répartition des principaux sols. Le chapitre 6 traite de l'utilisation des terres et des aptitudes des sols à l'agriculture.

Le tableau des *associations de sols* énumère toutes les unités cartographiques dans l'ordre alphabétique des symboles. Les autres colonnes indiquent:

Les sols associés

Les inclusions

Les phases

La superficie des unités en milliers d'hectares

La répartition par pays.

La *répartition des principaux sols* est traitée sur la base de trois grandes zones pédologiques — hautes terres, basses terres, et les Caraïbes — et figure sur une carte à petite échelle (figure 6). Les principaux sols de chaque région sont étudiés en fonction des facteurs du milieu, et leurs principales caractéristiques sont exposées.

L'étude de l'*utilisation actuelle des terres et de leur vocation agricole* est accompagnée d'un exposé sur les systèmes de culture traditionnels et modernes. On passe ensuite à l'examen des principaux sols pris séparément; leur utilisation actuelle et leur aptitude à l'agriculture tant traditionnelle que moderne sont décrites.

Настоящий том посвящен мексиканской и центральноамериканской части Почвенной карты мира масштаба 1:5 000 000. Составление почвенной карты Мексики и Центральной Америки было завершено ФАО и ЮНЕСКО в соответствии с их совместным проектом, начатым в 1961 году.

Карты

Лист карты, представляющий почвенную карту Мексики и Центральной Америки, составлен на топографической основе карты Американского географического общества масштаба 1:5 000 000. Картографические единицы - это сочетания почвенных единиц, подразделяющихся на классы по механическому составу и условиям рельефа. Они показаны на карте индексами. Преобладающие почвы показаны окраской, а фазовые различия показаны наложенной штриховкой.

Небольшая карта-врезка показывает три степени надежности информации о почвах, на основе которой составлялась карта.

Детальные определения почвенных единиц и полные описания всех использованных терминов можно найти в томе I настоящего издания.

Текст

В первой главе описывается развитие проекта в Мексике и Центральной Америке и даются некоторые замечания по использованию карты. Во второй главе выражается благодарность за сотрудничество учреждениям и большому числу лиц, которые приняли участие в составлении карт и текста. В третьей главе дано краткое содержание первого тома относительно карт и легенды.

Основные главы данного тома посвящены условиям окружающей среды и использованию почв и земли.

УСЛОВИЯ ОКРУЖАЮЩЕЙ СРЕДЫ

Глава 4 содержит краткое описание, с картами, четырех факторов окружающей среды, которые имеют непосредственное отношение к географии почв: климата, растительности, геологии и литологии, рельефа.

Климат рассматривается на основе шести широких климатических подразделений. Поскольку критерии, использованные для выделения картографических единиц, те же, что и критерии, важные с точки зрения выращивания растений, то климатическая карта служит дополнением к почвенной при передаче информации по выращиванию культурных растений из одной части мира в другую. Здесь обсуждаются лишь наиболее высокие категории. Основные климатические регионы показаны на мелкомасштабной карте (фиг. 2).

Растительность рассматривается на основе двух широких климатических регионов: жаркой и умеренно-холодной зон. Она далее подразделяется в соответствии с высотой и широтой относительно никарагуанской депрессии, которая в целом разделяет флоры, характерные для Северной и Южной Америк. Соответствующие субрегионы показаны на мелкомасштабной карте (фиг.3). В тексте даны некоторые краткие замечания по каждому региону и по размещению и природе субрегионов.

Геология, рельеф и литология рассматриваются в отношении к основным формам поверхности. Рельеф (фиг.4) и литология (фиг.5) также обсуждаются в отношении к природе и распространению почвообразующих пород.

ПОЧВЫ И ИСПОЛЬЗОВАНИЕ ЗЕМЛИ

Глава 5, описывающая почвы Центральной Америки, Мексики и островов Карибского моря, содержит обширную таблицу почвенных сочетаний и сводку по распространению основных почв. В шестой главе рассматривается использование земли и пригодность почв для сельского хозяйства.

Таблица почвенных сочетаний содержит все картографические единицы в алфавитном порядке индексов. Другие колонки показывают:
сочетающиеся почвы
включения
фазы
площади выделов в 1000 га
страны распространения

Распространение основных почв рассматривается на основе крупных почвенных регионов, сгруппированных в низменности, возвышенности и горы и показанных на мелкомасштабной карте (фиг.6). Основные почвы каждого региона рассматриваются в связи с факторами окружающей среды, а также отмечены их важнейшие особенности.

Современное использование земли и пригодность для сельского хозяйства рассматриваются в общих чертах с учетом традиционных и современных систем земледелия. Затем основные почвы рассматриваются в отдельности. Описывается их современное использование, а также их пригодность как для традиционных, так и для современных систем земледелия.

En este volumen se describe la sección de México y América Central del Mapa Mundial de Suelos a escala 1 : 5 000 000. La compilación del Mapa de Suelos de México y América Central fue completada por la FAO y la Unesco en un proyecto conjunto iniciado en 1961.

Los mapas

La hoja con mapas que comprende el Mapa de Suelos de México y América Central se ha trazado sobre los mapas topográficos base de la serie a escala 1 : 5 000 000 de la American Geographical Society. Las unidades del mapa son asociaciones de unidades de suelos divididas en clases texturales topográficas o de inclinación. Se indican en el mapa por medio de símbolos. Los suelos dominantes se muestran por colores, mientras que las diferentes fases se indican con sobreimpresiones.

Un pequeño mapa en recuadro indica tres grados de fiabilidad de la información sobre los suelos que sirvió de base para la compilación del mapa (Figura 1).

En el Volumen I de la serie (Leyenda) pueden encontrarse las definiciones detalladas de las unidades de suelos y descripciones completas de todos los términos utilizados.

El texto

En el primer capítulo se describe el desarrollo del proyecto en México y América Central y se dan algunas notas sobre los usos del mapa. En el segundo, se da cuenta de la cooperación de organismos y del gran número de personas que han colaborado en los mapas y en el texto, y en el tercero se presenta un sumario del material contenido en el Volumen I sobre los mapas y la leyenda.

Los capítulos más importantes de este volumen tratan de las condiciones del medio, de los suelos, del aprovechamiento de las tierras y de la aptitud de los suelos.

CONDICIONES DEL MEDIO

El Capítulo 4 contiene breves reseñas, con mapas, de los cuatro factores del medio que guardan una estrecha relación con la estructura de los suelos: el clima; la vegetación; la geología; y la fisiografía y litología.

Clima: Se estudia sobre la base de seis amplias subdivisiones. Ya que los criterios que se han seguido para la delimitación de las unidades son aquéllos que tienen importancia para el desarrollo de los cultivos, el mapa climático sirve así de complemento del mapa de suelos para la transferencia de información sobre cultivos de una parte del mundo a otra. Aquí sólo se examinan las categorías superiores. Las principales regiones climáticas se señalan en un mapa a pequeña escala (Figura 2).

Vegetación: Se estudia sobre la base de 15 amplias regiones de vegetación que se señalan en un mapa a pequeña escala (Figura 3). El texto contiene breves notas sobre las condiciones ecológicas, las principales especies de plantas y la distribución de las regiones de vegetación.

Geología, fisiografía y litología: Se examinan en relación con las formas principales del terreno. La fisiografía (Figura 4) y la litología (Figura 5) se estudian también en relación con la naturaleza y distribución del material de partida de los suelos.

LOS SUELOS Y EL USO DE LA TIERRA

El Capítulo 5, en que se describen los suelos de México y América Central, contiene un extenso cuadro de las asociaciones de suelos y una reseña de la distribución de los suelos principales. En el Capítulo 6 se estudia el uso de la tierra y la aptitud de los suelos para la agricultura.

El *cuadro de asociaciones de suelos* enumera todas las unidades del mapa por orden alfabético de los símbolos. En las otras columnas se presentan:

Suelos asociados

Inclusiones

Fases

Superficie de las unidades en millares de hectáreas

Países en que se presentan

Distribución de los suelos principales: Se examina sobre la base de tres regiones generales de suelos (tierras altas continentales, tierras bajas continentales y suelos de las Antillas), señaladas en un mapa a pequeña escala (Figura 6). Los suelos principales de cada región se estudian en relación con los factores del ambiente, indicándose sus características más importantes.

El *uso actual de la tierra y su aptitud para la agricultura:* Se examinan de un modo general, dándose una relación de los sistemas de labranza tradicionales y modernos. Se consideran después por separado los principales suelos, describiéndose su uso actual y la aptitud de la tierra para la labranza tanto tradicional como moderna.

1. INTRODUCTION

History of the project [1]

Recognizing the need for an integrated knowledge of the soils of the world, the Seventh Congress of the International Society of Soil Science, held at Madison, Wisconsin, United States in 1960, recommended that ways and means be found for the publication of soil maps of the great regions of the world. As a follow-up to this recommendation, FAO and Unesco agreed in 1961 to prepare jointly a Soil Map of the World based on the compilation of available soil survey material and on additional field correlation. The secretariat of the joint project was located at the headquarters of FAO in Rome. It was responsible for collecting and compiling the technical information, undertook correlation studies, and drafted the maps and text.

In June 1961 an advisory panel composed of prominent soil scientists representing various parts of the world was convened by FAO and Unesco to study the methodological, scientific and various other problems related to the preparation of a Soil Map of the World. [2]

Some of the earliest investigations into tropical soil genesis and soil interrelationships in the western hemisphere began in the Caribbean sector of this region. The pioneer of scientific soil studies was undoubtedly J.B. Harrison, who before the turn of the century had reported on the genesis of a fertile soil in Barbados and had published an account of the rocks and soils of Grenada and Carriacou islands.

---

[1] This section refers mainly to the preparation of the Soil Map of Mexico and Central America. The history of the project as a whole is dealt with more completely in Volume I.

[2] The participants at this meeting were:

Consultants: G. Aubert (France), M. Camargo (Brazil), J. D'Hoore (Belgium), E.V. Lobova (U.S.S.R.), S.P. Raychaudhuri (India), G.D. Smith (United States), C.G. Stephens (Australia), R. Tavernier (Belgium), N.H. Taylor (New Zealand), I.V. Tiurin (U.S.S.R.), F.A. Van Baren (Netherlands).

Unesco Secretariat: V.A. Kovda and M. Batisse.

FAO Secretariat: D. Luis Bramão, R. Dudal and F. George.

Four decades later came the studies by F. Hardy, A. Rodriguez and C.F. Charter, which added greatly to the soil knowledge of the Caribbean islands and some of the Central American countries. R.L. Pendleton, in 1945, was the first to try to convey a general picture of the soils of Central America, based on his own travels and information supplied by a growing body of national soil surveyors in the Central American countries. Mexico was the first country in the region to organize a team of soil specialists to report more specifically on the soils of areas where irrigation schemes might be implemented, an activity that led directly to the publication of the Soil Map of Mexico by M. Brambila in 1958.

A first draft of a soil map for Mexico and Central America was compiled by A.C.S. Wright. This map was based on information supplied by the national surveyors of the various countries and on correlation studies carried out by A. Smyth, N. Mikenberg, W.C. Bourne, C. Simmons, and R.F. Valencia.

Field correlation studies by A. Van Wambeke, K.J. Beek, A.C.S. Wright and R. Dudal, and further investigation of the nature of Mexican soils by a national group organized by G. Flores Mata, made it possible to draw a second draft of the soil map in 1967. This map was presented at the Ninth Congress of the International Society of Soil Science, held in Adelaide, Australia in 1968.

Finally, a third draft of the map was prepared in Rome in 1970 by A.C.S. Wright and R. Dudal. The main sources of additional soil information for this final draft are described in Chapter 3.

Objectives

Transfer of knowledge and experience from one area of the earth to another can only be successful when allowance is made for similarities and differences in the geographic, soil and climatic conditions

1

of the regions or countries involved. Furthermore, the economic feasibility of different management techniques under prevailing socioeconomic conditions needs to be assessed before they can be recommended for adoption. Reliable information on the nature and distribution of the major soils of the world is thus of fundamental importance. However, the preparation of regional and continental soil maps requires a uniform legend and nomenclature and the correlation of existing soil classification systems. One of the principal objectives of the FAO/Unesco Soil Map of the World project was to promote agreement among soil scientists all over the world on an international soil correlation system.

Agricultural research in Latin America is centred mainly on increased output from croplands and from pastures. Vast areas exist, however, which have scarcely been touched by man and are only now being studied to evaluate their future role in growing food for the rapidly increasing population. Many experts under international and bilateral programmes are assisting the governments in this task. This continental soils study attempts to present a synthesis of the knowledge available at the present stage of development of soil science in Mexico and Central America. It is hoped that it will promote better understanding among soil scientists, planners and farmers, provide useful coordination of national and international soils work and stimulate research and its application in the region.

Value and limitations of the map

The Soil Map of Mexico and Central America is meant to be a source of factual data, providing a basis and framework for further regional and national soil surveys at a more detailed scale. It may assist in selecting methods for reclamation, crop production, fertilizer application, and general use of soils. Up till now all attempts to make overall plans or forecasts for agriculture have been hampered by lack of uniformity in the terminology, nomenclature and classification of soils, and by lack of a comprehensive picture of the world's soil resources.

Through a systematic interpretation of the Soil Map of the World it will be possible to make an appraisal of the distribution and the production potential of the major soils on a continental basis and to delineate broad priority areas which deserve further study. This inventory of soil resources will bring to light the limitations and potentials of the different regions for increased food production.

In addition, a soil map such as the Soil Map of Mexico and Central America can be a valuable teaching aid for the training of geographers, soil

scientists, agronomists and all those who are involved with the study of the environment.

Although the publication of the map and text marks a significant step forward, it is necessary to point out its inherent limitations. The accuracy and detail of the information which can be shown are obviously limited by the small scale of the map and by the fact that soil data for some areas are scarce because of inadequate field correlation or lack of direct observations. In addition, difficulties were encountered in the compilation of the map because of the differences in the methods of field and laboratory studies. These limitations may also apply to the interpretive data, since they can only be as accurate as the soils information on which they are based. Despite these shortcomings, this soil map is the most recent and detailed inventory of soil resources based on international cooperation. Its limitations emphasize the necessity for intensified soil correlation and for obtaining better knowledge of the nature and distribution of soils in those parts of the continent where information is lacking or inadequate.

Use of the map and explanatory text

Against the background of the topographic base the map shows the broad pattern of dominant soils, marked by different colours. Clusters of closely related colours have been used for soils which have similar characteristics so that major soil regions can be recognized.

More detailed information about each mapping unit can be derived from the soil association symbols. The composition of the soil associations is given in Chapter 5, in which they are listed alphabetically and numerically, together with areas and location. A table showing the composition of the soil associations is also given on the back of the map.

The meaning of the classes for texture and topography which accompany the symbols of the mapping units is also explained on the soil map, as is the explanation of the overprints which indicate phases. These are further described in Chapter 3. The definitions of the soil units involved can be found in Volume I. The profile descriptions and analytical data in the Appendix illustrate and further clarify the soil definitions.

The geographical distribution of the soils is given in Chapter 5. For this purpose the continent has been subdivided into three major physiographic units: the highlands, the lowlands and the Caribbean islands. These units have been subdivided into 14 broad soil regions.

For information on the occurrence, land use, limitations, suitabilities and potentials of the soil units Chapter 6 should be consulted. Here the specific management problems of the soil units are discussed.

Those who are interested not only in the nature, distribution and suitabilities of the soils, but also in the natural environment, will find additional reading in Chapter 4. This chapter deals with climate, with vegetation (which in wide areas of Mexico and Central America can still be observed in its natural state), with geology, and with physiography (supplementing information in the chapter on the distribution of soils) and lithology.

2. ACKNOWLEDGEMENTS

The preparation of the Soil Map of Mexico and Central America could be accomplished only with the cooperation of many soil scientists and government institutions who provided basic material and took an active part in the meetings, study tours and discussions that led to the various drafts of the map and text.

Those who gave particular help to the project are listed below. Sincere appreciation is also expressed here to all those it has not been possible to single out.

Contributors

OFFICIAL AGENCIES

Ministry of Agriculture, Bahamas

Ministry of Agriculture, Science and Technology, Barbados

Ministry of Agriculture, Lands and Cooperatives, British Honduras

Ministerio de Agricultura y Ganadería, Costa Rica

Academia de Ciencias, Instituto de Suelos, Cuba

Ministerio de Agricultura, Dominican Republic

Ministerio de Agricultura y Ganadería, Sección de Suelos, El Salvador

Office de la Recherche Scientifique et Technique Outre-Mer, France

Ministerio de Agricultura, Departamento de Suelos, Guatemala

Secrétairerie de l'Etat de l'Agriculture, Haiti

Ministerio de Recursos Naturales, Departamento de Suelos, Honduras

Ministry of Agriculture and Fisheries, Jamaica

Secretaría de Recursos Hidráulicos, Jefatura de Irrigación y Control de Rios, Dirección de Agrología, Mexico

Foundation for Scientific Research in Surinam and the Netherlands Antilles, Netherlands

Stichting voor Bodemkartering, Netherlands

Ministerio de Agricultura y Ganadería, Departamento de Suelos, Nicaragua

Ministerio de Agricultura y Ganadería, Dir. Gen. de Recursos Naturales, Departamento de Suelos, Panama

University of Puerto Rico, Faculty of Agriculture, Puerto Rico

University of the West Indies, Faculty of Agriculture, Department of Soil Science, Trinidad

Directorate of Overseas Surveys, Land Resources Division, United Kingdom

National Cooperative Soil Survey of the United States of America

Organization of American States, United States

Unión Panamericana, Unidad de Recursos Naturales, United States

INDIVIDUAL CONTRIBUTORS

(by country to which their work relates)

British Honduras	A.C.S. Wright[1]
Costa Rica	C. Debehault,[1] H.W. Fassbender,[1] P. Guerra,[1] E. Knox,[1] J. Mannix, J.A. Martini[1]
Cuba	A. Hernandez, O. Portuondo, A.C.S. Wright,[1] V.I. Zonn
Dominican Republic	G.A. Tirado
El Salvador	C.W. Bourne,[1] S. Molina, M.A. Rico
French Antilles	M. Colmet-Daage

---

[1] FAO staff.

4

Guatemala	J.A. Gonzalez, J. Perdomo, C.S. Simmons[2]
Haiti	P. Pahaut[2]
Honduras	V. Castellanos, C. Eerkens,[2] C.S. Simmons[2]
Mexico	K.J. Beek,[2] E. Benítez, M. Brambila, D. Cabello Vega, G. Flores Mata, M. Macías, J. Martinez Alanis, L.A. Martinez, J. Meza Falliner, R.O. Monasterio, H. Quiñones, R. Rodríguez, A.C.S. Wright[2]
Netherlands Antilles	C. Veenenbos
Nicaragua	E. Marín Castillo, N. Mikenberg,[2] A. Prego, R.F. Valencia[2]
Panama	P. Guerra,[2] J.M. Mendez Lay, R. Tejeira
Puerto Rico	G. Smith

Preparation of the map

In close cooperation with the government institutions listed above, soil specialists, and FAO field staff, three successive drafts of the Soil Map of Central America, Mexico and the Caribbean islands were prepared at the FAO project centre in Rome.

Grateful acknowledgement is made of the permission given by the American Geographical Society of New York to use its 1 : 5 000 000 World Map as a basis for the preparation of the Soil Map of the World.

Preparation of the explanatory text

The explanatory text was prepared by A.C.S. Wright. The section on climate was prepared by C. Debehault. The sections on physiography and geology were prepared by J.H.V. van Baren and P.L.J. de Jongh. The section on vegetation, for Mexico, was drawn from a recent publication by G. Flores Mata *et al.*, and for the other countries of the area was compiled by C. Debehault.

---

[2] FAO staff.

Soil correlation

Considering the diversity of the basic material used and the different approaches applied to soil classification in different countries, soil correlation has been an essential aspect in the preparation of the Soil Map of Mexico and Central America.

Interterritorial soil correlation studies in the region were initiated by F. Hardy, C.F. Charter and R.L. Pendleton, but the first attempt at matching soils across an international boundary was made by C.S. Simmons and A.C.S. Wright in 1953, when the soils of the Petén region of Guatemala were correlated with the contiguous soils of British Honduras. In 1963, FAO promoted the first systematic soil correlation studies when A. Smyth (FAO, Rome), C.S. Simmons (FAO, Honduras), N. Mikenberg (FAO, Nicaragua), and C. Bourne (U.S. Technical Aid in El Salvador), together with the soil surveyors of those countries, spent several weeks examining the soils of the central part of the continent. In 1965, an international soil correlation meeting was held in Mexico to discuss the correlation of mapping legends used in Canada, Mexico and the United States. Participants at this meeting were: M. Brambila (Chairman, Mexico), M.E. Austin (United States), L. Iturriaga (Mexico), A. Leahey (Canada), R.O. Monasterio (Mexico), F.P. Rodríguez (Mexico) and R. Dudal (FAO). Subsequently, field correlation within Mexico and between Mexico and the United States was carried out by G. Flores Mata (Mexico), J. Douglass (United States), L.G. Gile (United States), J.W. Hawley (United States), R. Dudal (FAO), A. Van Wambeke (FAO), K.J. Beek (FAO) and A.C.S. Wright (FAO).

The responsibility for intercontinental correlation, preparation of the international legend and definitions of soil units was entrusted to R. Dudal (FAO).

Financial support

The costs of the preparation and printing of the Soil Map of Mexico and Central America were shared jointly by FAO and Unesco. Acknowledgement is also made here to the Governments of Belgium and the Netherlands, which made the services of associate experts available to the project (from Belgium: C. Debehault, 1969-70; from the Netherlands: P.L.J. de Jongh, 1970-72).

3. THE MAP

Topographic base

The Soil Map of Mexico and Central America was prepared on the basis of the 1 : 5 000 000 topographic map series of the American Geographical Society of New York, assuming an average radius of the earth of 6 378 388 metres. A bipolar oblique conic conformal projection was used.

Areas of land surfaces measured directly on the map with a planimeter are subject to variations due to the projection of less than 8 percent. Distances between land points measured directly on the map are subject to errors of less than 4 percent. The accuracy can be greatly improved by use of the key map on the American Geographical Society map, which gives lines of equal scale departure and conversion tables based on mean scale departure ratio.

Map units

The map unit consists of a soil unit or of an association of soil units. The textural class is indicated for the dominant soil unit while a slope class reflects the topography in which the soil association occurs. Furthermore, the associations may be phased according to the presence of indurated layers or hard rock at shallow depth, stoniness, salinity and alkalinity. The soil units, classes and phases are defined in Volume I.

Each soil association is composed of dominant and subdominant soil units, the latter estimated to cover at least 20 percent of the delimited area. Important soil units which cover less than 20 percent of the area are added as inclusions.

The symbols of the mapping units show the soil unit, textural class and slope class as follows:

Soil units. The symbols used for the representation of the soil units are those shown in the list of soil units on the back of the map. They are listed also in Table 1.

Textural classes. The textural classes, coarse, medium and fine, are shown by the symbols 1, 2 and 3 respectively.

Slope classes. The slope classes, level to gently undulating, rolling to hilly, and strongly dissected to mountainous, are indicated by the letters a, b and c respectively.

Cartographic representation

SYMBOLS

The soil associations have been identified on the map by the symbol representing the dominant soil unit, followed by a figure which refers to the descriptive legend on the back of the map in which the full composition of the association is outlined.

Example: Lc25   Chromic Luvisols and Luvic Kastanozems

Vp32   Pellic Vertisols, Vertic Luvisols and Eutric Regosols

Associations in which Lithosols are dominant are identified by the Lithosol symbol I combined with the symbol for one or two associated soil units.

Example: I-Bd   Lithosols and Dystric Cambisols

I-Re-Ne   Lithosols, Eutric Regosols and Eutric Nitosols

Where there are no associated soils or where the associated soils are not known, the symbol I is used alone.

If information on the texture of the surface layers (upper 30 cm) of the dominant soil is available the textural class figure follows the association figure, separated from it by a dash.

Example: Lc25-3   Chromic Luvisols, fine textured, and Luvic Kastanozems

Tm5-2   Mollic Andosols, medium textured, and Vitric Andosols

Where two groups of textures occur that cannot be delimited on the map two figures may be used.

Example: Y9-1/2   Yermosols, coarse and medium textured, and Lithosols

6

TABLE 1. — SOIL UNITS FOR MEXICO AND CENTRAL AMERICA

J FLUVISOLS	T ANDOSOLS	K KASTANOZEMS	W PLANOSOLS
Je Eutric Fluvisols	To Ochric Andosols	Kh Haplic Kastanozems	We Eutric Planosols
Jc Calcaric Fluvisols	Tm Mollic Andosols	Kk Calcic Kastanozems	Wd Dystric Planosols
Jd Dystric Fluvisols	Th Humic Andosols	Kl Luvic Kastanozems	Wh Humic Planosols
Jt Thionic Fluvisols	Tv Vitric Andosols		Ws Solodic Planosols
		H PHAEOZEMS	
G GLEYSOLS	V VERTISOLS	Hh Haplic Phaeozems	A ACRISOLS
Ge Eutric Gleysols	Vp Pellic Vertisols	Hl Luvic Phaeozems	Ao Orthic Acrisols
Gc Calcaric Gleysols	Vc Chromic Vertisols		Af Ferric Acrisols
Gd Dystric Gleysols		B CAMBISOLS	Ah Humic Acrisols
Gm Mollic Gleysols	Z SOLONCHAKS	Be Eutric Cambisols	Ap Plinthic Acrisols
Gh Humic Gleysols	Zo Orthic Solonchaks	Bd Dystric Cambisols	Ag Gleyic Acrisols
Gp Plinthic Gleysols	Zg Gleyic Solonchaks	Bh Humic Cambisols	
		Bk Calcic Cambisols	N NITOSOLS
R REGOSOLS	S SOLONETZ	Bc Chromic Cambisols	Ne Eutric Nitosols
Re Eutric Regosols	Sg Gleyic Solonetz	Bv Vertic Cambisols	Nd Dystric Nitosols
Rc Calcaric Regosols			
Rd Dystric Regosols	Y YERMOSOLS	L LUVISOLS	F FERRALSOLS
	Yh Haplic Yermosols	Lo Orthic Luvisols	Fo Orthic Ferralsols
I LITHOSOLS	Yk Calcic Yermosols	Lc Chromic Luvisols	Fr Rhodic Ferralsols
	Yl Luvic Yermosols	Lv Vertic Luvisols	Fa Acric Ferralsols
Q ARENOSOLS		Lf Ferric Luvisols	Fp Plinthic Ferralsols
	X XEROSOLS	Lp Plinthic Luvisols	
Qc Cambic Arenosols	Xh Haplic Xerosols	Lg Gleyic Luvisols	O HISTOSOLS
Qa Albic Arenosols	Xk Calcic Xerosols	P PODZOLS	Oe Eutric Histosols
E RENDZINAS	Xl Luvic Xerosols	Po Orthic Podzols	Od Dystric Histosols
		Pl Leptic Podzols	

Where information on relief is available the slope classes are indicated by a small letter, a, b or c, immediately following the textural notation.

Example: Lc25-3b   Chromic Luvisols, fine textured, and Luvic Kastanozems, rolling to hilly

In complex areas where two types of topography occur that cannot be delimited on the map two letters may be used.

Example: Kh21-2ab   Haplic Kastanozems, medium textured, and Luvic Yermosols, level to rolling

If information on texture is not available, then the small letter indicating the slope class will immediately follow the association symbol.

Example: I-Bd-c   Lithosols and Dystric Cambisols, steep.

MAP COLOURS

The soil associations have been coloured according to the dominant soil unit. Each of the soil units used for the Soil Map of the World has been assigned a specific colour. The distinction between map units is shown by a symbol on the map.

The colour selection is made by clusters so that "soil regions" of genetically related soils will show up clearly.

If insufficient information is available to specify the dominant soil unit, the group of units as a whole is marked by the colour of the first unit mentioned in the list (for example, the colour of the Haplic Yermosols to show Yermosols in general; the colour of the Ochric Andosols to show Andosols in general).

Associations dominated by Lithosols are shown by a striped pattern and by the colour of the associated soils. If no associated soils are recognized (because they occupy less than 20 percent of the area or because specific information is lacking) the colour of the Lithosol unit is applied uniformly over the hatched pattern.

PHASES

Phases are indicated on the Soil Map of the World by overprints.

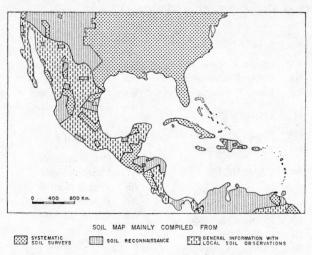

SOIL MAP MAINLY COMPILED FROM

SYSTEMATIC SOIL SURVEYS   SOIL RECONNAISSANCE   GENERAL INFORMATION WITH LOCAL SOIL OBSERVATIONS

Figure 1. Sources of information

The *duric, fragipan, petric* and *petrocalcic* phases show the presence of indurated layers, respectively duripan, fragipan, concretionary horizons and petrocalcic horizons, within 100 cm of the surface.

The *stony* phase marks areas where the presence of gravels, stones, boulders or rock outcrops makes the use of mechanized agricultural equipment impracticable.

The *lithic* phase indicates the presence of hard rock at less than 50 cm from the surface.

The *saline* phase shows that certain soils of the association (not necessarily the dominant ones) are affected by salt to the extent that they have a conductivity greater than 4 mmhos/cm in some part of the soil within 125 cm of the surface for some part of the year. The phase is intended to mark present or potential salinization.

The *sodic* phase is used for soils which have more than 6 percent saturation with sodium in some part of the soil within 125 cm of the surface. It should be noted that Solonchaks are not shown as saline phases and Solonetz as sodic phases, since these soils are saline and sodic, respectively, by definition. It follows that saline phases plus Solonchaks should be identified for all areas with saline soils, and sodic phases plus Solonetz for all areas with alkali soils.

Where more than one of these phases applies, only the one causing the strongest limitations for agricultural production has been shown.

MISCELLANEOUS LAND UNITS

Miscellaneous land units are used to indicate salt flats, dunes and shifting sand.

Where the extent of the land unit is large enough to be shown separately the sign may be printed over a blank background. If the land unit occurs in combination with a soil association the sign may be printed over the colour of the dominant soil.

Sources of information

A map showing the sources of information of the Soil Map of Mexico and Central America (Figure 1) is shown as an inset on the soil map. A distinction is made between the areas compiled from systematic soil surveys, soil reconnaissance, and general information with local field observations.

In the preparation of the soil map a large number of documents was consulted. It is impossible to mention them all. The most important, which cover substantial areas of the map or which were prepared specifically for the project, are recorded here by the country of origin.

BARBADOS

Soil map of Barbados. Soil and Land-use Survey, No. 18. Trinidad, Imperial College of Tropical Agriculture, 1966.

BRITISH ANTILLES

Soil maps of Antigua and Barbuda. Soil and Land-use Surveys No. 19 A and B. Trinidad, Imperial College of Tropical Agriculture, 1966.

Soil map of Grenada and Carriacou. Soil and Land-use Survey No. 9. Trinidad, Imperial College of Tropical Agriculture, 1959.

Soil map of Dominica. Soil and Land-use Survey No. 23. Trinidad, Imperial College of Tropical Agriculture, 1967.

Soil map of St. Kitts and Nevis. Soil and Land-use Survey No. 16. Trinidad, Imperial College of Tropical Agriculture, 1966.

Soil map of St. Lucia. Soil and Land-use Survey No. 20. Trinidad, Imperial College of Tropical Agriculture, 1966.

Soil map of St. Vincent. Soil and Land-use Survey No. 3. Trinidad, Imperial College of Tropical Agriculture, 1958.

Soil map of Montserrat. Soil and Land-use Survey No. 22. Trinidad, Imperial College of Tropical Agriculture, 1967.

BRITISH HONDURAS

Soil map of British Honduras. Report of British Honduras Land Use Survey. London, Colonial Research Publication No. 24, 1959.

COSTA RICA

Mapa de Suelos, Región Oriental de la Meseta Central. San José, Ministerio de Agricultura e Industria, 1954.

Mapa de Suelos, Región Occidental de la Meseta Central. San José, Bol. Téc. No. 22. Ministerio de Agricultura e Industria, 1958.

CUBA

Soil map of Cuba. Tropical Plants Research Foundation and U.S. Department of Agriculture, Washington, D.C., 1928.

DOMINICAN REPUBLIC

Soil map of Dominican Republic. Survey of the Natural Resources of the Dominican Republic. Washington, D.C., Organization of American States, 1969.

EL SALVADOR

Levantamiento General de Suelos. San Salvador, Ministerio de Agricultura y Ganadería, 1960.

FRENCH ANTILLES

Carte de Sols de la Guadeloupe. ORSTOM, Bureau des Sols des Antilles, 1960.

GUATEMALA

Mapa de Suelos de Guatemala - Clasificación de Reconocimiento de los Suelos de la República de Guatemala. Guatemala, Ministerio de Agricultura e Instituto Agropecuario Nacional, Departamento de Suelos, 1959.

HAITI

Caractéristiques et nature de la fraction argileuse de quelques sols rouges d'Haïti situés sur calcaires durs, par Colmet-Daage, F. *et al.* ORSTOM. *Pédologie,* 7(3), 1969.

HONDURAS

Informe al Gobierno de Honduras sobre los suelos de Honduras. Rome, FAO, 1969. AGL-UNDP/TA 2630.

JAMAICA

Soil maps of parishes. Soil and Land-use Surveys Nos. 1, 4, 7, 8, 10, 11, 12. Trinidad, Imperial College of Tropical Agriculture, 1958-61.

MEXICO

Carta general de grandes grupos de suelos. Sec. Rec. Hidráulicos 1958

Carta de suelos de la República Mexicana. Sec. Rec. Hidráulicos 1960

NETHERLANDS ANTILLES

Soil map of St. Maarten, St. Eustatius and Saba. Utrecht, Foundation for Scientific Research in Surinam and Netherlands Antilles, 1955.

NICARAGUA

Estudios ecológicos para aprovechamiento de la tierra en Nicaragua. FAO. Ministerio de Economía, Instituto de Fomento Nacional, 1959

Mapa de suelos del área del Proyecto de irrigación de Rivas. Managua, Ministerio de Agricultura y Ganadería, 1961.

PANAMA

Land classification and general soil map. U.S. Department of Agriculture, Washington, D.C., Office of Foreign Agricultural Relations, 1952.

PUERTO RICO

Soil map of Puerto Rico. U.S. Department of Agriculture, Bureau Chem. and Soils. Puerto Rico, University of Puerto Rico Agricultural Experimental Station, 1942.

TRINIDAD AND TOBAGO

Soil map of central Trinidad. Directorate of Colonial Surveys, 1954.

Profile description and analytical data for the soils of Tobago. Land Capability Survey of Trinidad and Tobago, Trinidad.

4. ENVIRONMENTAL CONDITIONS

In this chapter brief outlines are given of four aspects of the environment that are important in the development of soils. These are climate, vegetation, geology, and physiography and lithology.

These outlines, each of which is accompanied by a small-scale map, indicate the location and nature of the major regions in which important variants of climate, vegetation, landscape and rock types occur.

CLIMATE

The area discussed extends between latitudes 7°30′ and 32°30′N, that is from the subequatorial zone to the temperate zone.

It can be subdivided into two main regions:

1. Central America proper, southern Mexico and the Caribbean islands, with a tropical, isothermal and humid climate.

2. Central and northern Mexico, with a semitropical, continental and dry climate.

Climatic factors

Because of the mountainous nature of the terrain standing as a barrier between two major oceanic weather systems, changes from one climatic type to another are abrupt. But even if the land bridge had been of more subdued relief, there would still remain significant climatic differences between the northwestern and southeastern regions, between the Pacific and Atlantic coastal regions, and between the warm temperate northern latitudes and the tropical southern latitudes.

The northern and northwestern parts of the land bridge fall strongly under the influence of continental air movements from the high pressure centres of the North American continent. In this region dry continental climatic regimes dominate, contrasting with

regimes that are basically humid and isothermal (characterized by one or sometimes two periods with diminished rainfall). The dry seasons are more pronounced, more prolonged, and more regular in time of onset along the Pacific side of the land bridge because the moist oceanic air mass must first traverse a wide belt of cold ocean currents before it impinges on the land. This is not the case on the Atlantic side, where the sea currents are warm. Instead, the Atlantic lowlands are subject to periodic invasions of cold fronts, bringing cool air as southward extensions of the cold winter system of the North American continent. Occurring at any time from October to March, their onset and frequency is highly irregular from year to year.

The influence of these incursions of cool air along the eastern seaboard extends as far south as northern Honduras. The lower air temperatures during these winter months give rise to a variation in the typical isothermal humid tropical climate which is distinct from the normal subtropical climate and which has been variously called "extratropical," "quasitropical" and "semitropical." In this account they will be referred to as semitropical, implying that they are endowed with truly tropical temperature conditions for three quarters of the year but have enough cool, wet or damp days to limit the production of some tropical crops.

The climatic contrast between the Pacific and Atlantic lowlands is most pronounced above latitude 22°N. On the Pacific side, near the border with the United States, there is a small belt with a warm Mediterranean temperate climate, succeeded by a temperate subdesertic climate with winter rains grading into a warm maritime subtropical desertic climate which covers most of Baja California south of latitude 30°N. This is succeeded by a semitropical subdesertic climate, which in turn gives way to a humid-to-dry tropical climate near latitude 20°N. On the Atlantic side a very dry semitropical climate occurs south of the United States border and grades into a humid-to-dry semitropical climate before reaching latitude 20°N.

Between 15°N and 20°N there is greater similarity in lowland climates between the Pacific and Atlantic sides. Both have humid-to-dry and very dry tropical climates, but on the Atlantic lowlands the pattern of rainfall is much more erratic and winter temperatures may be low for a truly tropical climate. Over the wide plains of the Yucatán peninsula, elevation is so close to sea level that the rainfall pattern is as erratic as over the open ocean. South of latitude 15°N, the contrast between Pacific and Atlantic lowlands becomes once more pronounced with equatorial and subequatorial tropical climates predominating on the Atlantic side, and humid tropical climates on the Pacific side. On the Pacific side these climates have two pronounced dry seasons. On the Atlantic side there is one rather weakly defined dry season.

Going inland from the coast, the land rises, rainfall generally increases, and temperatures fall. This is particularly noticeable on the Atlantic side where the coastal plains are often wide and show a decreasing rainfall gradient between the coast and the foothills. Over the foothills rainfall increases steadily, culminating in a zone of cool, damp highlands with characteristic woodland vegetation and specialized agriculture, well exemplified by the crest of the Sierra Madre Oriental in Mexico. On the Pacific side the land rises more abruptly near the coast, and a moist highland environment occurs only in a few favoured places.

The climates of the interior uplands, highlands and valleys are varied. They can be shown only broadly on the accompanying climatic map (Figure 2). They include humid and dry isothermal, subtropical climates; warm temperate climates (tierra templada), some of which are semicontinental; medium to cold temperate climates (tierra fría); subdesertic and desertic upland climates (mainly in northern Mexico), and many intergrades which are too local to show on the small-scale map. Interior valleys with a northwest-southeast alignment generally show vertical zoning in which the climate changes with every few hundred feet of altitude, while valleys running deep into the ranges from either of the coasts show more gradual changes toward the interior. Many interior valleys experience subdesertic conditions at some point along the valley floor.

The islands of the Caribbean, subject for a large part of the year to the influence of the southeast trade winds, naturally show a marked climatic difference between the windward and leeward coasts. The former are much drier and the latter more uniformly moist, but not as moist as the central mountainous mass. Many of the small coral reef islands of very low relief are uniformly subdesertic. Only some of the larger islands (Cuba, Hispaniola, Jamaica, for example) show a more complex climatic pattern, with humid-to-dry tropical climates at lower elevations, very humid semitropical climates at higher elevations, and relatively dry interior valley climates.

Climatic regions

The classification used in this study is a synthesis of several other climatic and ecological systems, especially those of Köppen, Holdridge, Beard, Taylor and Gaussen. The limits are defined on the basis of distribution of natural vegetation and crops.

Figure 2 shows the climatic regions as they fall into large divisions A, B, C, D, K, L, M, S and T. The key showing subdivisions of each category and the factors determining the assignment into categories are given in Table 2.

The climatic regions have been grouped for convenience in six large classes:

1. Tropical (A)
2. Subtropical (B)
3. Warm temperate (C)
4. Medium and cold temperate (D)
5. Subdesertic (K, L, M)
6. Desertic (S, T)

Both thermal and rainfall types enter into the classification. Thermal types are defined by the mean annual temperature (MAT); the mean temperature for the coldest month (CMT); and the mean temperature for the warmest month (WMT). Rainfall types are defined on the basis of the number of dry months and the mean annual rainfall (MAR). A dry month is defined[1] in relation to thermal types as follows:

Tropical and semitropical regions: less than 60 mm MAR

Subtropical and temperate regions: 40-60 mm MAR subtropical, and 30-50 mm MAR temperate.

1. TROPICAL (A)

These climates have an MAT greater than 23°C, a CMT of 20°C or over, an MAR of more than 550 mm, and a maximum of 8 dry months. The length of the dry season is generally related to the amount of

_____

[1] Köppen's method is used for tropical and semitropical regions, and Gaussen's for subtropical and temperate. Gaussen's system is to call a month dry if the mean monthly rainfall in centimetres is less than twice the mean monthly temperature in °C.

11

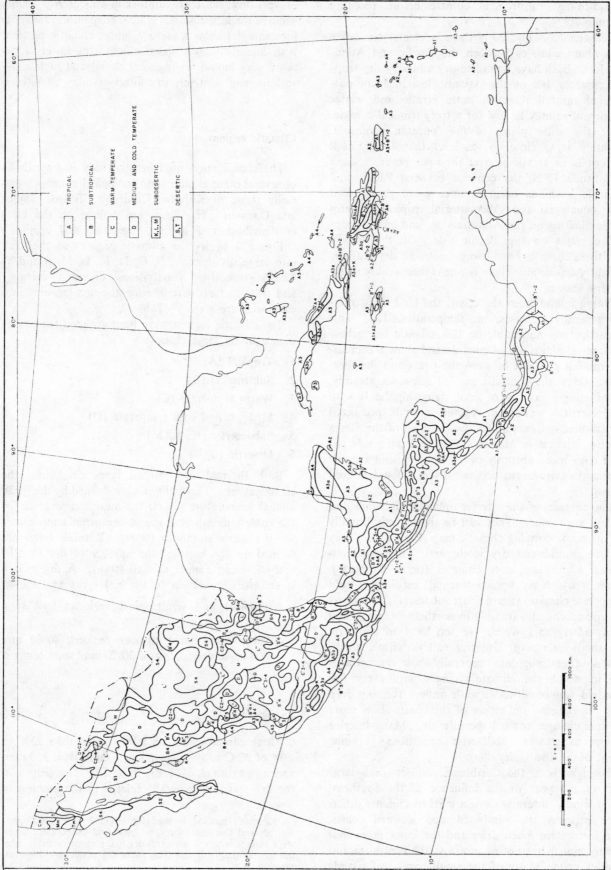

Figure 2. Climatic regions

annual rainfall and coincides with the coldest part of the year.

Tropical climates occupy by far the greatest surface of Central America, Mexico, and the Caribbean area. On the basis of the length and intensity of dry season, four tropical climatic types have been distinguished.

A1 and A2. The very humid or equatorial climate (A1) is characterized by high rainfall (over 60 mm monthly) during the whole year. In contrast, the humid tropical climate (A2) has 1-3 dry months (with mean monthly rainfall less than 60 mm). Regions with A1 and A2 climates support the evergreen rainforest.

A3. This is a humid to dry tropical climate characterized by well-defined dry and humid seasons, with 4-6 dry months. A3 regions support a deciduous tropical forest; in fact the boundary between A2 and A3 is established by the passage from evergreen to semideciduous forest. Cuba is almost entirely A3, as are the centre and south of Haiti and the coastal regions of the other islands.

A4. In the very dry tropical A4 climates there is a dry season of 6-8 months. A4 regions generally have a bush savanna with many xerophytes.

2. SUBTROPICAL (B)

Transitional between tropical and temperate, the subtropical climate is not well defined. The semitropical climates where cooling is caused by latitude are shown by B.

B'' indicates the subtropical climates where cooling is caused by altitude.

B' shows the subtropical climates combining both effects: the semitropical climates of altitude.

B'' climates are continuations on higher altitudes of the tropical climates. They differ from the B climates in their much lower summer temperatures and lower monthly average temperature, between 18 and 23°C. Near the upper limit of these climates, corresponding approximately to the frostline, frost may occur if there is a well-defined dry season.

The B' climate occurs as an extension to the north of the B'' climate as well as an extension to higher altitudes of the B climate. It is characterized by an MAT between 18 and 23°C, a CMT of less than 14°C and an MAR of more than 500 mm. In contrast to B and B'', the B' climate may have rather severe frosts.

B1 and B2. These are respectively the very humid and humid semitropical climates. Rainfall characteristics are the same as those of the A1 and A2 climates, but the mean temperature of the coldest month is lower. Frost does not occur. These climates support evergreen forests. They occupy a relatively small area on the lower northern slopes of the Sierra Madre Oriental from Punta Delgada to the latitude of Ciudad del Maíz.

B3. The humid to dry semitropical climate is characterized by 4-6 dry months. Frost does not occur, but minimum temperatures are near zero. This climate occupies the plains along the Gulf, northeast of the Sierra Madre Oriental to about latitude 23° N, and small areas in the mountains of Sinaloa, in central Cuba, and in the north of the Bahamas.

B4. This very dry semitropical climate is characterized by 6-8 dry months and an MAR between about 550 and 1 000 mm, or 9 dry months. The coldest monthly temperature is between 16 and 20° C. There are sporadic frosts. B4 climate occurs on both the Atlantic side, from latitude 22° N up to Texas, and the Pacific side between latitudes 24 and 28° N. It does not occur in the Antilles.

Combinations of B' and B'' with B1, B2, B3 and B4 are distinguished on the map (Figure 2).

3. WARM TEMPERATE (C)

These climates have an MAT between 16 and 18° C. In Central America they are nearly always extensions of subtropical climates at higher altitudes. Only the extreme northwest of Mexico has a Mediterranean type of temperate climate at sea level. Several subdivisions have been distinguished.

The C'' climates are isothermal warm temperate climates (upper tierra templada). They have the same rainfall pattern as the isothermal tropical climate B'' but occur at higher altitudes. MAR is more than 400-500 mm, and may be more than 5 000 mm. Frosts occur, especially at higher elevations. According to the length of the dry season, two climates have been distinguished, C''1-2 and C''3-4.

C''1-2. These are the very humid to humid isothermal warm temperate climates (included in B''1-2 on the map), and a continuation of the B''1 and B''2 climates. They are characterized by a dry season of 0-3 months and a mean annual rainfall of more than 1 300 mm. They support a thick, evergreen forest, rich in epiphytes and ferns, but are very little inhabited because of the excessive humidity. Only the regions with relatively low rainfall (about 1 500-1 600 mm) have some population. Rainfall may go as high as 5 000 mm.

C''3-4. These are humid to very dry isothermal warm temperate climates, and are the continuation

TABLE 2. — KEY TO CLIMATIC MAP OF MEXICO AND CENTRAL AMERICA

CLIMATE	Symbol on map	Mean annual temperature	Mean temperature in coldest month	Mean temperature in warmest month	Annual amplitude	Frost	Mean annual rainfall	Number of dry months
		.... Degrees centigrade					*Millimetres*	
Tropical (A)		>23	≥20	(>24)→ +30	1→10 (generally 1→7)	None	>550→ +6 000	≤8
A1 Very humid or equatorial	A1	>23	≥20	<30	1→6	None	>1 900→ +6 000	0
A2 Humid	A2	>23	≥20	<30	1→7	None	>1 500→ +3 000	1→3
A2a Subequatorial variety......	A2a	>23	≥20	<30	1→7	None	>2 500	1→2
A3 Rather humid to dry	A3	>23	≥20	<30	1→8	None	>1 250→ +2 000	4→6
A3a Dry variety .	A3a	>23	≥20	<30	4→8	None	>1 000→1 250	6
A4 Very dry	A4	>23	≥20	≤30	4→10	None	>550-600→1 000	6→8-9
Subtropical (B)								
B Semitropical		>23	<20(but>14)	>27→ +31	8→17°	Very sporadic, light	>550-600	≤8
B1 Very humid	B1-2	>23	17→20	<30	8→10	None	1 700→ +2 000	0
B2 Humid	B1-2	>23	17→20	<30	8→10	None	1 400→1 900	1→3
B3 Rather humid to dry	B3	>23	17→20	≤30	8→10	Extremely sporadic, light	>1 000-1 100	4→6-7
B4 Very dry	B4	>23	14→20	>28→ +32	10→17	Very sporadic, light	550-600→1 000	6→8-9
B4a Variety with two dry seasons..	B4a	>23	14→19	>28→ +32	12→17	Very sporadic, light	600→800 with a second dry season in summer	7→8
B″ Isothermal		18→23	>14	<25-26	1→8-10	Very sporadic, light	>500-550→ +6 000	≤8
B″1 Very humid	B″1-2	18→23	>14	<25-26	1→8-10	None	> 2 000→ +6 000	0
B″2 Humid	B″1-2	18→23	>14	<25-26	1→8-10	None	> 1 400→ +3 000	1→3
B″3 Rather humid to dry	B″3	18→23	>14	<25-26	1→8-10	Extremely rare	>950-1000→+2500	4→6
B″4 Very dry	B″4	18→23	>14	<25-26	3→8-10	Extremely rare	>500, <950-1 000	6→8
B′ Semitropical of altitude		18→23	< 14	>26	10→20	Rather frequent, light to strong	>500	≤8
B′3 Rather humid to dry	B′4	18→23	10→14	26→ +31	10→20	Rather frequent, light to strong	>1 000	4→6
B′4 Very dry	B′4	18→23	10→14	26→ +31	10→20	Rather frequent, light to strong	>500→1 000	6→8
Warm temperate (C)		15→18						≤8
C″ Isothermal		16→18	12→16	17→21-22	1→9	Possible, sometimes frequent	>400-450→ +5 000	≤8
C″1-2 Very humid to humid .... (mapped with B″1-2)	C″1, C″1-2	16→18	12→16	17→21-22	1→8	Very light, rare	1 300→ +5 000	0→3
C″3-4 Rather humid to very dry........	C″3-4	16→18	12→16	17→21-22	1→9	Stronger, more frequent	>400-450→ +2 000	4→8

TABLE 2. — KEY TO CLIMATIC MAP OF MEXICO AND CENTRAL AMERICA

CLIMATE		Symbol on map	Mean annual temperature	Mean temperature in coldest month	Mean temperature in warmest month	Annual amplitude	Frost	Mean annual rainfall	Number of dry months
			.... *Degrees centigrade*					*Millimetres*	
C,C'	SEMICONTINENTAL AND CONTINENTAL		16→18	<12	>21-22	(9→20)	Rather frequent	>400	≤8
C'2-4	Humid to very dry semicontinental	C2-4	16→18	9-10→12	21→25	(9→15)	Possible, rather severe	400→1 000	3→8
C4	Very dry continental	C2-4	16→18	5→10	25→28	(15-20)	Severe	400-500	6→8
Cm	MEDITERRANEAN		<18	>5				Winter rains, dry summers	1→8
Cm4	Very dry maritime	Cm	15-18	9-13	19-24	±10	Very sporadic, light	>250-300 250-350	8
Medium and cold temperate (D)			<16						
D''1-4	Very humid to very dry isothermal	D	12→16	9→13	14→20	1→10	Rather strong	>300 >+2 000	0→8
D-D'1-4	Very humid to very dry semicontinental and continental	D	12→16	4→11	17→24	10→20	Very strong	>300→+1 500	0→8
Subdesertic (K, L, M)									8→10-11
K	Tropical	K	>23	≥20	(>26-27)	4→10	None	<550-600 >300	11
L	Semitropical	L	>23	<20 (13→20)	>28→+32	10→18	Light to severe	<550 >250-300	11
L'	Continental	L'	18→23	<14 (10→14)	>26→+30	(10→18)	Severe	<500 >250	11
L''	Isothermal	L''	18→23	>14	<26 (21-26)	6→10	Light	<500 >250	11
M	Temperate with summer rains, isothermal, semicontinental, continental	M	<18	5→16	17→28	(±10)→+20	Light to severe	<300-400 >200-250	11
Mm	Mediterranean, with winter rains	Mm	15-18	9→14	20→25	(+10)	Very sporadic	150-250	9→11
Desertic (S, T)									11-12
S1	Warm semitropical	S1	>23	≤20 (15-20)	>28→+31	10-16	None	<250 (40→250)	11
S2	Warm maritime semitropical	S2	18→23	>15 (15-19)	<30 >26	8-14	None	<250 (50→250)	12
S3	Warm continental semitropical	S3	18→23	10→14	≥30→+32	>15	Very light to rather severe	≤250 (40→250)	12
S4	Semitropical	S4	18→23	10→16	25→30	10-15	Light to very severe	≤250-300 (50→350)	12
T	Warm continental temperate	T	16→18	5→10	25→28	±20	Very severe	<200-250	11-12
Tm	Maritime Mediterranean temperate	Tm	15-18	10→14	20→25	(±10)	None or very light	Rainfall in winter <150-200	11

of the B″3 and B″4 climates at higher altitudes, with 4-8 dry months and a mean annual rainfall of more than 400 mm. They are much more widespread than C″1-2 climates. All the higher mountains of the interior and western part of Central America are C″3-4. The characteristic vegetation is pine forest.

C2-4. These are semicontinental and continental warm temperate climates, and are continuations to the north of the C″ climates. They occur in the mountains and plateaus of northern Mexico, where latitude combined with continentality results in lower winter and higher summer temperatures. CMT is less than 12° C and WMT higher than 21-22° C.

Cm. This is a warm Mediterranean temperate climate, characterized by rainfall in the cold season and dryness in the warm season. It is therefore distinguished from all types discussed before by an inverse rainfall regime.

4. MEDIUM AND COLD TEMPERATE (TIERRA FRIA) (D)

These climates are characterized by an MAT between about 12 and 16° C. Rainfall and length of dry season are variable: MAR ranges from 300 to more than 1 500 mm and the number of dry months from 0 to 8.

D climate generally occurs above 2 000 m on the highest mountains of Central America and Mexico.

Two subdivisions of D climate are distinguished in Table 2: isothermal (D″) and continental (D′). The isothermal is characterized by a WMT of 14-20° C and a CMT from 10 to 13° C. The absolute minimum can be —5 °C or even less.

In the semicontinental and continental, D and D′, coldest and warmest averages are more extreme. Chihuahua, with a continental type climate, has the coldest winters of the whole of Central America, with absolute minima varying from —11 to —20°C.

The D climates support forests of pines and even firs, more or less mixed with oaks, except in Talamanca where only oaks occur.

5. SUBDESERTIC (K, L, M)

These climates are defined by a dry season of from 8 to 10-11 months with an approximate mean annual rainfall between 300 and 550 mm in the tropical climates, between 250-300 and 500 mm in the subtropical climates, between 250 and 400 mm in the warm temperate climates, and between 200-250 and 300 mm in the medium and cold temperate climates.

Subdesertic climates occur mostly in Mexico, in vast areas in the north. In Central America and the Antilles they occur only in very small areas, generally valleys protected by high mountains.

All these climates support a bush vegetation of xerophytes (acacias, cactus).

On the basis of the thermal regime several subdivisions are distinguished.

K. *Tropical subdesertic*

This climate corresponds to A climates, except that rainfall is lower, less than 550-600 mm. It is limited to small areas, nearly always protected valleys.

L. *Semitropical subdesertic*

This climate has an MAT higher than 23°C and a CMT less than 20°C. It differs from the B4 climate in the lower rainfall, which is less than 550 mm.

L′. This is a continental semitropical subdesertic climate. Rainfall is lower than in L climates. MAT lies between 18 and 23°C. Rather severe frosts can occur. There is no well-defined wet season. The L′ climate occurs over vast areas of the plateaus of central and northern Mexico.

L″. This isothermal subtropical subdesertic climate has the same MAT as the L′, but the annual amplitude is less. It corresponds to the B″4 climate, except that there is less rainfall. Light sporadic frost can occur.

M. *Temperate subdesertic with summer or winter rains*

This climate is defined by a mean annual temperature of less than 18°C. The type characterized by summer rains has an MAR of less than 300-400 mm and is characteristic of the eastern slopes of the Sierra Madre Occidental and the plateaus of Zacatecas-San Luis Potosí.

The variant, Mm, is characterized by winter rains with lower annual mean rainfall and 9-11 dry months.

6. DESERTIC (S, T)

These climates are defined by a dry season of 10-11 to 12 dry months with a mean annual rainfall of less than 250-300 mm in the semitropical regions, less than 200-250 mm in the temperate regions with summer rains, and less than 150-200 mm in the temperate regions with winter rains.

They support only very poor vegetation. Many areas have no vegetation at all.

According to the thermal and rainfall characteristics, six subdivisions are distinguished and are listed in Table 2. The four S climates are semitropical, and the two T climates are temperate.

VEGETATION

Although the total area is not extensive, the climatic and physiographical conditions in Mexico and Central America are extremely varied. Vegetation types therefore range from desert formations to dense tropical forests.

A description of 15 broad types of natural vegetation follows. Their distribution is given in Figure 3. The description for Mexico has been taken from a recent publication, Flores Mata, G. *et al.*, *Tipos de vegetación de la República Mexicana*, 1971, and the area covered by such vegetation in other countries of Central America and the Caribbean islands has been compiled from existing literature.

1. HYDROPHILOUS VEGETATION

This consists of vegetative communities rooted in swampy areas subject to flooding by shallow fresh or brackish water.

Mangrove (Miranda and Hernández X., 1963; Rzedowski and McVaugh, 1966)

This is a community of simple floristic composition. Its height generally ranges from 3 to 5 m and may reach 25 m.

It occurs on the low muddy shores of the coasts of both oceans and is characteristic of estuaries and river mouths; it also occurs in areas nearby where the soil is of alluvial origin and is periodically flooded by brackish water without strong surf.

The commonest tree on the Gulf coast is the red mangrove (*Rhizophora mangle*) with stilt-shaped aerial roots. Nearer solid ground the white mangrove (*Avicennia germinans*) predominates, characterized by aerial roots which emerge from the mud in the shape of sails. In sandy zones or areas of nearly fresh water the dominant species is the buttonwood (*Conocarpus erecta*).

Popal

This is a type of herbaceous vegetation which grows in hot climates in water approximately 1 m deep. The plants have long narrow leaves which emerge from the water, and the most common species belong to the genera *Calathea* and *Thalia*. In shallower water grasses of the genera *Leersia*, *Paspalum*, *Panicum*, *Oryza*, *Zizaniopsis* and *Hymenachne* abound.

Tules and reeds

These are communities of herbaceous plants on lands covered by shallow water. The stems generally have long narrow leaves, but are sometimes leafless. The genera and species forming these dense groupings are tule (*Typha* spp.), reed grass (*Phragmites communis*), *Scirpus californicus*, *Cyperus giganteus* and others. They occur in temperate or hot climates on the shores of lakes, lagoons, streams and rivers.

2. PALMS

This group consists of plants commonly called palms, corozo, manaca, mishero palm, tepejilote and guano, which occur in regions of hot or temperate climate and varying degrees of humidity, frequently in coastal areas. The leaves are pinnatifid or fan-shaped.

The commonest species are corozo (*Scheelea liebmanni*), manaca (*Scheelea preussii*), royal palm (*Roystonea* sp.), coquito de aceite (*Orbignya guacoyule*), *Sabal morrisiana*, apachite palm (*Sabal mexicanum*), *Pseudophoenix sargentii*, *Paurotis wrightii*, *Brahea dulcis* and *B. calcarea*, and *Washingtonia* spp.

3. SAVANNA

In its most characteristic form this group is composed of grasses without trees or with scattered trees. Such grasses occur in hot zones with poorly drained soils which become muddy in the rainy season and extremely dry during the period of minimum rainfall. The commonest trees are the golden spoon (*Byrsonima crassifolia*), the sandpaper (*Curatella americana*), and the calabash (*Crescentia alata* and *C. cujete*).

In general, the grasses are tufted, tough and fire-tolerant and belong to the genera *Paspalum*, *Andropogon*, *Trichachne*, *Imperata*, *Trachypogon* and *Manisuris*.

4. TALL FOREST

This type of forest formation is composed of trees more than 30 m high. Its composition is complex and it occurs in hot climates with average annual temperatures exceeding 20ºC, an annual rainfall of over 1 200 mm and generally deep soils. It is found on the slopes of the Gulf of Mexico and the Pacific.

Tall evergreen forest

This is a very dense type of vegetation with abundant lianas and epiphyte plants. All or most of the trees remain green throughout the year, although some occasionally shed their leaves during flowering. It occurs in areas where the average annual rainfall is over 1 500 mm and there is a very short dry season or none at all.

There are numerous variations in floristic composition, the commonest trees being *Terminalia amazonia*, mahogany (*Swietenia macrophylla*), the ramón

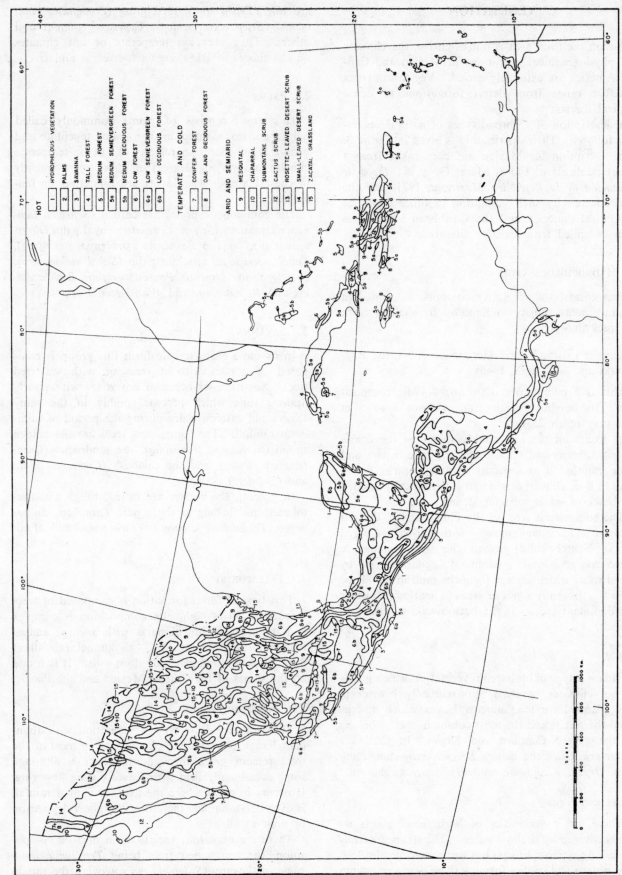

HOT				TEMPERATE AND COLD		ARID AND SEMIARID	
1	HYDROPHILOUS VEGETATION			7	CONIFER FOREST	9	MESQUITAL
2	PALMS			8	OAK AND DECIDUOUS FOREST	10	CHAPARRAL
3	SAVANNA					11	SUBMONTANE SCRUB
4	TALL FOREST					12	CACTUS SCRUB
5	MEDIUM FOREST					13	ROSETTE-LEAVED DESERT SCRUB
5a	MEDIUM SEMIEVERGREEN FOREST					14	SMALL-LEAVED DESERT SCRUB
5b	MEDIUM DECIDUOUS FOREST					15	ZACATAL GRASSLAND
6	LOW FOREST						
6a	LOW SEMIEVERGREEN FOREST						
6b	LOW DECIDUOUS FOREST						

Figure 3. Broad vegetation regions

18

breadnut tree (*Brosimum alicastrum*), *Vochysia guatemalensis*, macayo (*Andira galeottiana*), amates (*Ficus* spp.), *Dialium guianense*, *Inga* spp., *Calophyllum brasiliense*, the provision tree (*Pachira aquatica*), and *Terminalia oblonga*. In higher areas, between 700 and 1 500 m, calatola (*Calatola laevigata* and *C. mollis*), yoloxóchitl (*Talauma mexicana*), and oaks (*Quercus* spp.) are frequent.

The main areas occupied by this forest are the plains and slopes of the Gulf of Mexico and the Pacific, the region of Soconusco as far as Pijijiapan, the western part of Nicaragua and Panama and the western slopes of the Caribbean islands.

Tall semievergreen forest

From 25 to 50 percent of the trees composing this type of forest lose their leaves during the severest part of the dry season.

It occurs in areas with lower rainfall, in protected places like canyons, where average annual temperature is over 20ºC and rainfall is more than 1 200 mm per year.

The most conspicuous species are the ramón breadnut tree (*Brosimum alicastrum*), sapodilla (*Manilkara zapota*), tempisque (*Sideroxylon tempisque*), mahogany (*Swietenia macrophylla*), white mangrove (*Bucida buceras*), capiri (*Masticodendron capiri*), *Mirandaceltis monoica*, and *Carpodiptera floribunda*.

This formation is found principally in areas of the Gulf of Mexico and the Yucatán peninsula, and also in parts of the Pacific slope.

5. MEDIUM FOREST

The height of this type of forest varies from 15 to 30 m. It occurs in zones with an average annual temperature of over 20ºC, on both the Gulf of Mexico and Pacific slopes and in the Yucatán peninsula. The genera and species are extremely varied.

5a. MEDIUM SEMIEVERGREEN FOREST

The characteristic feature of this forest type is that some of the trees (25 to 50 percent) lose their leaves at the height of the dry season. The principal trees are of the same species as those of the tall semievergreen forest.

This type of vegetation covers extensive areas with an average annual temperature of over 20ºC and an average annual rainfall exceeding 1 200 mm. In areas of lower rainfall the *Brosimum* association grows in canyons, which are generally more humid.

Area of distribution includes the Gulf of Mexico and Pacific slopes and extensive areas in the Yucatán peninsula and Cuba.

5b. MEDIUM DECIDUOUS FOREST

Many of the trees composing this forest (75 percent or more) lose their leaves at the height of the dry season.

The climate in which this forest grows has an average annual temperature of over 20ºC, with an annual rainfall of around 1 200 mm and a pronounced dry season. It is usually found on moderately deep soils and frequently coexists with low deciduous forest or savanna, but occupies the water meadows of rivers or streams (gallery forest).

The most characteristic species are the courbaril (*Hymenaea courbaril*), conacaste (*Enterolobium cyclocarpum*), red cedar (*Cedrela mexicana*), cacahuanache or totoposte (*Licania arborea*), primavera (*Tabebuia donell-smithii*) and jabilla (*Hura polyandra*).

6. LOW FOREST

This is made up of trees 15 m or less in height. Depending on the climatic conditions in which they occur, they wholly or partly lose their leaves in the dry season. This forest is found in hot, humid or semidry climates.

6a. LOW SEMIEVERGREEN FOREST

The characteristic feature of this forest is that 25 to 50 percent of the trees composing it lose their leaves in the dry season. It is usually found on deep soils with poor drainage, so that trees typical of savanna sometimes occur. The most characteristic genera and species are *Acacia pennatula*, *Ateleia* spp., *Vitex* spp., *Lonchocarpus* spp., *Coccoloba* spp., coyol (*Acrocomia mexicana*), logwood (*Haematoxylon campechianum*), white mangrove (*Bucida buceras*) and chechem (*Metopium brownei*).

This forest is distributed mainly within the Yucatán peninsula in low depressions, and on the slopes of the Gulf of Mexico and the Pacific.

6b. LOW DECIDUOUS FOREST

This forest occurs in climates with an average annual temperature of over 18ºC, and a long dry season when all or most trees shed their leaves. Numerous variants occur in its area of distribution. The commonest species are *Piscidia piscipula*, wild tamarind (*Lysiloma bahamensis*), cópite or siricote (*Cordia dodecandra*), *Alvaradoa amorphoides*, brazilwood (*Haematoxylon brasiletto*), *Lysiloma gellermanni*, *L. acapulcensis*, ceiba (*Ceiba acuminata*), copal (*Bursera excelsa*), pistachio (*Pistacia mexicana*), cuachalalá (*Amphipterygium adstringens*), *Bursera* spp., copalcocote (*Cyrtocarpa procera*), *Ipomoea* spp. and navío (*Conzattia sericea*).

19

Species of thorny Leguminosae are sometimes abundant. The most important of these are mezquite verde, palo verde or palo mantecoso (*Cercidium* spp.), ebony (*Pithecolobium flexicaule*) and desert ironwood (*Olneya tesota*).

Bouteloua curtipendula, *B. rothrockii*, *Hilaria semplei* and *Cathestecum* spp. are common in the herbaceous stratum.

Low deciduous forest is widely distributed and covers parts of the Yucatán peninsula, the basins of the Balsas and Papaloapán rivers, the Tehuantepec isthmus, Chiapas and the slopes of the Sierra Madre Oriental and the Sierra Madre Occidental.

7. CONIFER FOREST

This includes all the communities constituted by the different genera of the order Coniferales, of which *Pinus* and *Abies* are the most important in Mexico.

The distribution and ecological conditions of these communities are extremely broad and varied, although they form the largest stands in the mountain chains of the central, eastern and western parts of Mexico, in temperate and cold climates and on thin and rocky or deep soils, the latter being the most frequent condition.

Oyamel forest

This corresponds to the fir and oyamel forest of Miranda and Hernández X. (1963). It is composed basically of the genus *Abies* of which several species exist, the commonest being *Abies concolor* of the Baja California peninsula, *A. durangensis* in the north of Mexico, *A. religiosa* in the centre and *A. guatemalensis* in the south.

Its area of distribution is more or less the same as for pines, but it occupies smaller areas, nearly always at heights of 2 000 to 3 000 m in humid zones.

Cedar and juniper forest

Although less important than the fir and pine forests, this type of community may be well defined in some areas. It is composed mainly of the genera *Cupressus* and *Juniperus*, which usually have the same area of distribution as pines and oyamels, although they are still more restricted in the area they occupy. This forest sometimes occurs in lower, dryer zones with different degrees of salinity.

Pine forest

This forest grows in a wide variety of soils and climates, at altitudes of from 300 to 4 000 m. Its area of distribution corresponds approximately to the main highlands and elevations in Mexico. In the north are found chiefly the species *Pinus arizonica*, *P. chihuahuana*, *P. cooperi*, *P. engelmannii*, *P. durangensis*, *P. jeffreyi*, *P. quadrifolia* and *P. cembroides*; in the centre and south of the country *P. montezumae*, *P. pseudostrobus*, *P. douglasiana*, *P. tenuifolia*, *P. leiophylla* and *P. michoacana* abound; *P. patula* occurs in the Sierra Madre Oriental and *P. oocarpa* in the Sierra Madre del Sur.

Pine-oak forest

This type of forest is composed of numerous species of pine (*Pinus*) and oak (*Quercus*), in varying proportions. Its area of distribution is very broad, especially in the main mountain chains of Mexico.

8. OAK AND DECIDUOUS FOREST

Oak forest

This consists of dense forests formed mainly of oaks (*Quercus*). The species vary greatly from one place to another depending on geographical position and ecological conditions. The denser and taller forests occur in the humid parts of the mountainous regions in the centre and south of Mexico.

The species *Quercus insignis*, *Q. strombocarpa*, *Q. oocarpa*, *Q. corrugata*, *Q. skinneri* and others are found in very humid and semihot localities. *Quercus trinitatis*, *Q. acatenangensis*, *Q. laurina*, *Q. rugosa*, *Q. crassipes*, *Q. mexicana*, *Q. candicans*, *Q. affinis* and others, occur on the Gulf and Pacific slopes and in the mountainous interior.

Quercus oleoides, *Q. sororia* and *Q. glaucescens* are frequent in hot zones. In areas of transition between zones of temperate and hot climates *Q. glaucoides*, *Q. macrophylla*, *Q. magnoliaefolia*, *Q. urbani*, *Q. crassifolia* and *Q. brachystachys* are often found.

Quercus chihuahuensis, *Q. emoryi*, *Q. jaliscensis*, *Q. mohriana* and *Q. oblongifolia* are common in northern Mexico.

The distribution of oak forest is generally similar to that of pine and pine-oak forests.

Deciduous forest

The trees of this forest formation lose 75 percent or more of their leaves during the winter season.

They occur in areas similar, except for greater humidity, to those of some oak and pine forests.

Rzedowski and McVaugh (1966) call this type of vegetation mesophyllous mountain forest, a name originally proposed by Miranda (1947). Trees are 20 to 40 m high. The most characteristic species are American sweet gum (*Liquidambar styraciflua*), beech (*Fagus mexicana*), *Nyssa sylvatica*, *Carpinus caroliniana*, *Ostrya virginiana*, *Tilia mexicana*, *Ternstroemia pringlei*, *Oreopanax xalapensis*, *Bocconia ar-*

borea, Cornus disciflora, Myrica mexicana, communities of Lauraceae, *Weinmannia* and others. Miranda and Hernández X. (1963) also mention *Englehardtia, Meliosma* and *Podocarpus*. This forest occurs on the slopes of the Gulf of Mexico and the Pacific Ocean, but with differences in composition between one side and the other.

9. MESQUITAL

This low, thorny, evergreen forest vegetation is widely distributed from the south of Mexico to the desert zones of the north. In the less dry areas in the south the principal species is the mesquite *Prosopis juliflora* accompanied by camachile (*Pithecolobium dulce*), while in arid or subarid zones the mesquite *Prosopis laevigata* and *Prosopis* spp. predominate.

10. CHAPARRAL

Chaparral is composed of dense clusters of low oaks (*Quercus*), which are often associated with the genera *Adenostoma, Arctostaphylos, Cercocarpus, Amelanchier* and others. Its area of distribution lies in the zones of contact between groups of arid climates. It is most typically represented on the slopes of the Pacific in the northwest of the Baja California peninsula, although it also exists in Nuevo León, San Luis Potosí, in the south in the Mixteca Alta and in the Oaxaca valley.

Among the most common species may be mentioned *Quercus ceripes, Q. intricata, Q. microphylla, Q. potosina* and *Q. tinkhamii*.

11. SUBMONTANE SCRUB

This type of vegetation is more or less equivalent to the piedmont shrub of Müller (1939, 1947). It is characterized by tall shrubs or low trees from 3 to 5 m high, usually deciduous for a short period during the dry season. Leaves or folioles are small.

This vegetation is found on low hills, on low-lying areas in the highlands and on the eastern and western slopes of the northern Sierra Madre Oriental, at heights from 700 to 1 700 m, on shallow soil and limestone rock or rhyolite.

Species correspond to the genera *Acacia, Bernardia, Bonetiella, Bumelia, Celtis, Chiococca, Colubrina, Cordia, Decatropis, Eysenhardtia, Flourensia, Fraxinus, Gochnatia, Helietta, Krugiodendron, Lemaireocereus, Lindleyella, Lysiloma, Mimosa, Myrtillocactus, Neopringlea, Opuntia, Pistacia, Pithecellobium, Portlandia, Pseudosmodingium, Psidium, Sebastiania, Vauquelinia, Wimmeria* and *Yucca*. Müller (1939, 1947) also mentions *Quercus, Leucaena, Agave, Sophora, Bauhinia, Rhus* and *Diospyros*.

12. CACTUS SCRUB

This vegetation is characterized by the presence of large Cactaceae.

It is composed of communities of different species. The genus *Opuntia* (prickly pear) dominates, especially in the northern part of Mexico.

The species most commonly found in extensive areas of prickly pear are *Opuntia leucotricha, O. robusta*, and *O. steptacantha*. Groups of Cactaceae with cylindrical stems may be extensive, for example the chollas (*Opuntia fulgida* and *Opuntia* spp.) and the large sahuaro (*Carnegia gigantea*) of northwest Mexico; toward the centre of the country it is common to find pitayos or cardonas (*Lemaireocereus weberi, L. dumortieri*), teteche (*Neobuxbaumia tetetzo*), garambullo (*Myrtillocactus geometrizans*), chiotilla (*Escontria chiotilla*) and old-man cactus (*Cephalocereus senilis*).

Its area of distribution corresponds to the arid and subarid zones of the centre and north of Mexico.

13. ROSETTE-LEAVED DESERT SCRUB

This group corresponds mainly to the maguey, lechuguilla and guapilla vegetation (thorny plants with leaves arranged in the shape of a rosette) described by Miranda and Hernández X. (1963).

It is composed of shrub and subshrub species with long narrow leaves grouped in rosettes. It includes arborescent plants which have a well-developed stem or caudex and belong to the genera *Yucca* (palm or izote) and *Dasylirion* (sotol), and plants with a poorly developed stem and a set of leaves forming a rosette at the base, such as the genera *Agave* (maguey, lechuguilla) and *Hechtia* (guapilla).

Rosette-leaved desert scrub occurs on limestone and loamy slopes in high regions and descends as far as the upper parts of the alluvial fans at the base of the mountains. It can also occur on slight inclines where the soil contains abundant gravel and fragments of limestone rock.

The climate where this type of vegetation is found is similar to that for small-leaved desert scrub.

The dominant species are lechuguilla (*Agave lechequilla*), palma samandoca (*Yucca carnerosana*), candelilla (*Euphorbia antisyphilitica*), guayule (*Parthenium argentatum*), espadín (*Agave striata*), guapilla (*Hechtia glomerata*) and sotol (*Dasylirion* spp).

14. SMALL-LEAVED DESERT SCRUB

This is distinguished by the predominance of shrubby elements with small leaves or folioles. It occurs on level ground and in the lower parts and slopes of a large zone of the Altiplano and in the north, northeast and northwest of Mexico. In the state of San Luis Potosí, where this vegetation is extensive, the average annual temperatures are approximately 16 to 20°C and the rainfall recorded in some localities is 270 to 500 mm. The dry months in the year vary from 7 to 11.

The soils are of alluvial origin on deep deposits which have accumulated at the bottoms of valleys or depressions or on shallower and rather stony deposits in the lower parts of the alluvial fans at the base of hills. There is usually an indurated ironstone or calcium carbonate horizon.

This type of vegetation varies in floristic composition and the height of its components. Certain shrubs regularly lose their leaves while others are evergreen.

The creosote bush (*Larrea tridentata*) is the dominant species. Others include *Flourensia cernua*, *Allionia incarnata*, mesquite (*Prosopis laevigata*), granjeno (*Celtis pallida*), clavellina (*Opuntia leptocaulis*), and grasses in the herbaceous stratum.

15. ZACATAL GRASSLAND

This type of vegetation is made up of different grasses or grassy species. These are generally in groupings of highly homogeneous appearance although there may be shrubs or treelets. Two types of community are considered within this group.

Pastizal pasture

Pastizal is generally not as high as the zacatonal community (see below) and grows in temperate climates. The most extensive areas of pastizal are composed of groups of blue grama (*Bouteloua gracilis*), *Bouteloua eriopoda*, *B. chondrosoides*, *Muhlenbergia porteri*, *Lycurus phleoides* and *Sporobolus cryptandrus;* of tufted grasses such as *Heteropogon contortus*, *Bouteloua curtipendula*, *Elynurus barbiculmis;* and of buffalo grass (*Buchloe dactyloides*), *Bouteloua filiformis* and *Hilaria cenchroides*.

Species growing on saline and saline-sodic soils include *Sporobolus airoides*, tobosa (*Hilaria mutica*), salt grass (*Distichlis spicata*), and jihuite or zacahuistle (*Eragrostis obtusiflora*). *Bouteloua chasei* and *Sporobolus nealleyi* are found on gypseous soils.

Some areas of pastizal are composed of buffalo grass (*Buchloe dactyloides*), *Lycurus phleoides*, *Cathestecum* and *Opizia*. Cordgrass (*Spartina spartinae*) and *Sporobolus splendens* grow near the coasts.

Zacatonal pasture

This community is distinguished from pastizal by its tall tufted grasses.

The characteristic genera are *Stipa*, *Muhlenbergia*, *Calamagrostis* and *Festuca*. They occur in rocky or shallow soils on sloping ground, or in deep soils on level ground, in high cold zones of nearly all the great elevations of Mexico between the tree line and the alpine zone. They therefore occupy a very small area.

GEOLOGY

This section deals chiefly with geological aspects of the environment relating to land forms and to the nature and distribution of soil parent materials in the region.

One is accustomed to thinking of Central America as a land bridge linking the northern and southern continents of the western hemisphere. However, for most of geologic time the two continents were separate entities and they acquired their present linkage as a result of volcanic activity, probably late in the Mesozoic era. Prior to this time the margin of the northern continent extended southward to the latitude of Nicaragua and eastward to the longitude of Jamaica and beyond. The southern continent extended northeastward to Barbados, Aruba, Curaçao, Bonaire, Los Roques, and La Blanquilla. Between the two continental masses lay a deep extension of the Pacific Ocean, sometimes referred to as the " Caribbean Mediterranean. "

The Central American region was subjected to significant changes in the relative distribution of land and sea, reflecting a long history of geologic instability. The most stable area in the map region is thought to be the Precambrian platform underlying the Gulf of Mexico, extending from Florida to the Bahama islands. Around this stable platform, folding, faulting and volcanic activity have built up the present-day landscapes of southern Mexico and Central America.

To the west of the stable platform, the north-south Precambrian fold system of the western Cordillera of North America extended down to the latitude of central Mexico, there meeting another ancient protaxis extending eastward from the Pacific. This latter, an extensive transverse fold system, formed the Antillean geanticline. Between the mountains of the Antillean geanticline and the stable platform lay a zone of downwarped strata, the Antillean geosyncline, over which the erosion products from the Antillean ranges accumulated. In early Mesozoic time part of this geosynclinal trough was invaded by water from the Atlantic Ocean to form the Antillean sea.

The relative distribution of land and water established by the end of the Paleozoic era apparently endured, with only minor fluctuations, throughout most of the Mesozoic, until general subsidence and breaking up of the folded ranges during the Jurassic period. At this time the peneplaned rumps of the Antillean ranges were invaded by the sea and subsequently buried under thick layers of sediments, including an impressive thickness of limestone during the ensuing Cretaceous period.

The ancient east-west structural lines of the Antillean system became further obscured by a new system of fault lines trending mainly north-south, thrusting up segments of Paleozoic and later sediments as "horst" mountains, and depressing adjacent areas below the now extensive Antillean sea. The Maya mountains of British Honduras represent one small block-faulted tilted fragment of the ancient Antillean geanticline, and the adjacent Bay of Campeche represents a downfaulted area. Both lie at the southern margin of the stable platform. The northeast corner of the Maya mountain fault block may represent the oldest exposed land surface in Central America, standing as a small island above the Cretaceous sea and never subsequently submerged. Reactivation of these north-south fault systems, probably in the Pliocene epoch of the Tertiary period, may have extended the zone of uplift into the actual margin of the stable platform. There it formed a submarine ridge on which the Yucatán peninsula subsequently formed.

The sequence of geologic events at the northern limit of the South American continent shows some striking parallels. The dominantly north-south folded ranges of the Andes terminate in a series of east-west transverse folded mountains extending from the Pacific far out into the Atlantic. During the general subsidence of the land in Jurassic time, the northern borderland of the southern continent foundered, leaving only small block-faulted fragments now represented by the islands of Aruba, Curaçao and Bonaire. Mexico too was deeply submerged during the Jurassic and Cretaceous periods, but began to emerge during the Pliocene and Pleistocene epochs of the Tertiary period, along with the Gulf border of North America.

Widespread volcanic activity occurred in both the Cretaceous and Tertiary periods. It was during the former that the connexion between North and South America was formed at the site of Costa Rica and Panama. Many of the West Indian island chains were formed during Tertiary volcanic activity. "High" islands are mainly emergent volcanoes, but where submarine volcanic activity just failed to reach the surface of the sea the volcanic piles were generally capped with reef limestones. When these subsequently emerged, they became the "low" islands. On some of the high islands active volcanoes still exist. The extensive volcanic belt crossing central Mexico from coast to coast is partly of Cretaceous, partly of Tertiary origin, and several volcanoes are of Recent geologic age. The volcanic highlands extending from Guatemala south to Nicaragua are similarly of mixed chronology.

Geologic history clearly shows that the Central American map region comprises many relict fragments of the terminal parts of two major continental systems. These have been plastered over and joined together mainly by marine sediments, of Cretaceous age or younger. Volcanic island arcs and mountain chains add further diversity to the present-day landscape. Geologic history also emphasizes that the Caribbean islands (especially the larger ones) are an integral part of the Central American region, since they were once joined to it in the Antillean geanticline. Whereas man and other late forms of animal life knew Central America only as a land bridge between the continents, earlier forms of animal life and most plant life were able to disseminate in an east-west direction but were unable to cross by land between continents.

In terms of past climatic patterns, the absence of a warm Gulf stream until comparatively late in geologic time must certainly have affected weather in the northeastern sector of the map region. In terms of soil formation in ancient times, it is readily understandable why Ferralsols characteristic of old land surfaces have a very limited extension: no really ancient land surfaces have survived the complex series of geologic changes in the map region. Perhaps the oldest fragment of an ancient landscape surviving is that now represented by the northeastern corner of the Maya mountains in British Honduras. This small area may have been above the level of the sea from Cretaceous time onward. The oldest and least eroded soils of this ancient landscape are Humic Cambisols, not unlike those occurring near Itapeva, in the state of São Paulo, Brazil.

PHYSIOGRAPHY AND LITHOLOGY

On the basis of the geologic composition of present-day land surfaces, distinctive physiographical relationships can be identified. These are shown on the physiographical map (Figure 4) as follows:

A. Mountain ranges

B. Plateaus

C. Depressions

D. Plains

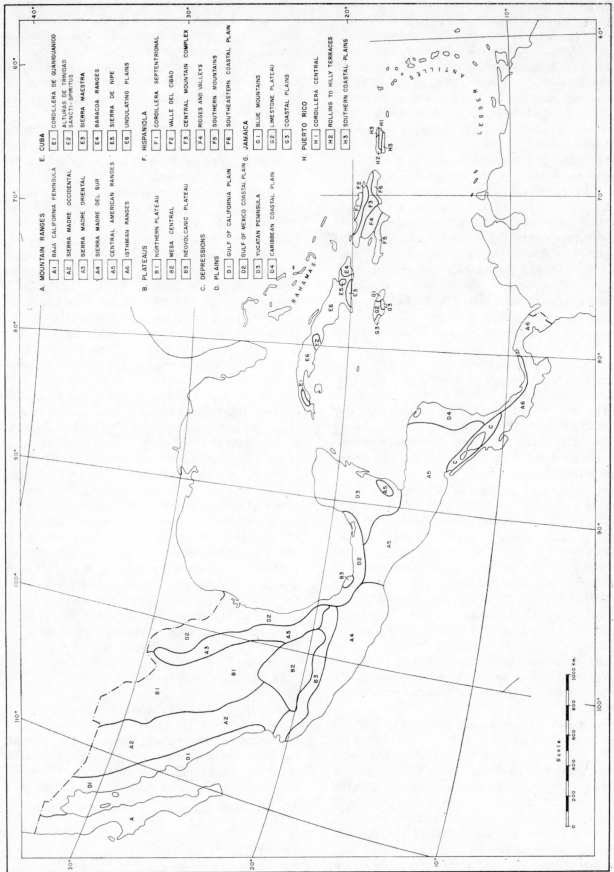

A. MOUNTAIN RANGES

A1 | BAJA CALIFORNIA PENINSULA
A2 | SIERRA MADRE OCCIDENTAL
A3 | SIERRA MADRE ORIENTAL
A4 | SIERRA MADRE DEL SUR
A5 | CENTRAL AMERICAN RANGES
A6 | ISTHMIAN RANGES

B. PLATEAUS

B1 | NORTHERN PLATEAU
B2 | MESA CENTRAL
B3 | NEOVOLCANIC PLATEAU

C. DEPRESSIONS

D. PLAINS

D1 | GULF OF CALIFORNIA PLAIN
D2 | GULF OF MEXICO COASTAL PLAIN
D3 | YUCATAN PENINSULA
D4 | CARIBBEAN COASTAL PLAIN

E. CUBA

E1 | CORDILLERA DE GUANIGUANICO
E2 | ALTURAS DE TRINIDAD SANCTI-SPIRITUS
E3 | SIERRA MAESTRA
E4 | BARACOA RANGES
E5 | SIERRA DE NIPE
E6 | UNDULATING PLAINS

F. HISPANIOLA

F1 | CORDILLERA SEPTENTRIONAL
F2 | VALLE DEL CIBAO
F3 | CENTRAL MOUNTAIN COMPLEX
F4 | RIDGES AND VALLEYS
F5 | SOUTHERN MOUNTAINS
F6 | SOUTHEASTERN COASTAL PLAIN

G. JAMAICA

G1 | BLUE MOUNTAINS
G2 | LIMESTONE PLATEAU
G3 | COASTAL PLAINS

H. PUERTO RICO

H1 | CORDILLERA CENTRAL
H2 | ROLLING TO HILLY TERRACES
H3 | SOUTHERN COASTAL PLAINS

Figure 4. Physiographic regions

24

In the case of the Caribbean islands, the scale of the map does not permit physiographical subdivision of any but the largest islands: Hispaniola (consisting of Haiti and the Dominican Republic), Cuba, Jamaica and Puerto Rico. The physiographical units are marked on the map by a letter denoting the island followed by a number for the dominant physiographical unit.

A grouping of lithologically similar rocks is the basis for a lithological map (Figure 5), which shows the distribution of the soil parent materials. The map distinguishes:

S1 Consolidated clastic sediments (sandstone, siltstone, shale, conglomerate)

S2 Consolidated carbonate sediments (limestone, dolomite, marl)

S3 Fluvial and lacustrine sediments, recent and unconsolidated

M Metamorphic rocks (gneiss, schist, phyllite, quartzite, slate)

I1 Acid intrusive rocks (granite, diorite, quartz-porphyry, syenite)

I2 Basic intrusive rocks (peridotite, serpentinite, gabbro, diorite, dolerite, pyroxenite, norite)

E1 Acid effusive rocks (rhyolite, dacite, quartz-porphyry, trachyte)

E2 Basic effusive rocks (basalt, andesite, dolerite, diabase).

The brief descriptions which follow of the physiographical units shown in Figure 4 include information on the main features of the lithographical pattern and the general nature of the soil-forming parent materials.

A. Mountain ranges

A1 Baja California peninsula
A2 Sierra Madre Occidental and adjacent Buried Ranges
A3 Sierra Madre Oriental
A4 Sierra Madre del Sur system
A5 Central American ranges
A6 Isthmian ranges and adjacent coastal plains

A1. BAJA CALIFORNIA PENINSULA

The backbone of this peninsula is a tilted fault block about 1 600 km in length, but seldom more than 60 km in width. The elevation in the north is over 3 500 m and diminishes to about 600 m north of La Paz in the south. The unit consists of a zone of mountains on the axis of the peninsula, partly covered with volcanic products in the centre and south. The coastal plain, with some lagoons, is mainly located on the Pacific side, while the side along the Gulf of California is largely bounded by cliffs. The islands and small peninsulas are formed by smaller faults.

The dissection is typical of deserts. The canyons have steep walls and the valleys are filled with sand. Waste-filled graben are common and many have volcanoes in them.

The more prominent individual mountain ranges are the San Pedro Mártir reaching nearly 4 000 m and the Sierra de la Giganta. South of La Paz a complex faulting produced the mountainous Sierra de San Lazaro, rising to more than 2 000 m. This region is less arid than the north and central parts of the peninsula, and the dissection is more normal.

Rhyolite lavas, breccias, and tuffs of mid-Cenozoic age are widespread throughout, with metamorphic sediments occurring in the Vizcaino peninsula. Batholithic granite rocks of Mesozoic age occur in the north and extreme south of the Baja California peninsula. The offshore bars along the Pacific suggest that the west coast of the peninsula emerged gradually.

Land of lower relief is mainly occupied by Pleistocene and Recent sediments, usually unconsolidated and partly aeolian in origin. Much of the hard rock of the region is also covered by Recent aeolian drift materials; these fine and coarse sands and silts are the dominant soil-forming parent materials of the ranges and foothills, extending outward over the lowlands with interspersed areas of lacustrine clays and salt plains.

A2. SIERRA MADRE OCCIDENTAL AND ADJACENT BURIED RANGES

This unit follows the western coast of Mexico and the Gulf of California at some distance inland and stretches southward for about 1 300 km from the border with the United States. It has in parts a width of about 300 km and is bordered in the east by the northern plateaus.

It comprises the Sierra Madre Occidental, the most prominent mountain range of the whole of Middle America, and its westerly extension, the Buried Ranges. This last sub-unit was formed by the movement of huge amounts of desert waste from the desertic highlands in a westerly direction, burying for a considerable distance the northwesterly ranges of the Sierra Madre Occidental. The Buried Ranges (part of which are known as the Sonoran high ranges) merge with the vast sloping plain of Sonora, Sinaloa, and Nayarit. Erosion by wind and

S1 CONSOLIDATED CLASTIC SEDIMENTS (SANDSTONE, SILTSTONE, SHALE, CONGLOMERATE)

S2 CONSOLIDATED CARBONATE SEDIMENTS (LIMESTONE, DOLOMITE, MARL)

S3 FLUVIAL AND LACUSTRINE SEDIMENTS, RECENT AND UNCONSOLIDATED

M METAMORPHIC ROCKS (GNEISS, SCHIST, PHYLLITE, QUARTZITE, SLATE)

I1 ACID INTRUSIVE ROCKS (GRANITE, DIORITE, QUARTZ-PORPHYRY, SYENITE)

I2 BASIC INTRUSIVE ROCKS (PERIDOTITE, SERPENTINITE, GABBRO, DIORITE, DOLERITE, PYROXENITE, NORITE)

E1 ACID EFFUSIVE ROCKS (RHYOLITE, DACITE, QUARTZ-PORPHYRY, TRACHYTE)

E2 BASIC EFFUSIVE ROCKS (BASALT, ANDESITE, DOLERITE, DIABASE)

Scale

0   200   400   600   800   1000 Km.

Figure 5. Lithological map

occasional flash floods is still occurring. Neither the western nor the eastern limits of the unit are distinct geographically.

The Sierra Madre Occidental, the most rugged and mountainous area of Mexico, attains a height of about 3 500 m in the centre and south and is never lower than about 2 000 m. It consists of a complex series of parallel mountain ranges, sweeping longitudinal valleys and short, deep, transverse valleys and canyons. The lava (rhyolite) plateau in the centre of the Sierra is about 800 km long and has elevations between 2 000 and 3 500 m. Undulations and rolling uplands are common, and most of the rivers are located at the bottom of shallow synclines. The edges of the plateau become increasingly dissected toward the west, where they form a mountainous flank of the Sierra Madre. They drop abruptly through a belt of spectacular gorges and deep valleys to the piedmonts.

Some canyons cut through the lavas into older rocks where ores are mined. The richest are the silver and gold mines, but also lead, zinc and copper are found here. The high plateaus are the main source of Mexico's lumber.

Lying between two desertic areas, the Sierra, because of its altitude, receives rain from east and west. Many rivers originate here and make it possible to use the Northern plateau and the Gulf of California coastal plain to economic advantage.

Acid rhyolitic lavas, breccias and tuffs of mid-Cenozoic age are again the commonest rocks of the map unit, with smaller areas of Triassic and Lower Cretaceous clastic and carbonate sediments occurring as islands in the volcanic rocks. Miocene to Recent sediments occur chiefly in valleys and small basins. A small area of Mesozoic metamorphic rocks occurs near Sinaloa. Basic intrusive rocks of mainly Tertiary age are common. Any of these rocks may be soil-forming, but the majority of soils are formed from desertic aeolian drift materials mixed with some volcanic ash.

A3. SIERRA MADRE ORIENTAL

This mountain range forms a highly dissected 700-km wall between the northern plateau and the coastal plain along the Gulf of Mexico.

It is a faulted, broken and eroded folded scarp margin of the northern plateau, its edges rising little above the level of the plateau on the west and its eastern slopes covered with coastal deposits. In the northern section the ranges are irregular but usually far enough apart to have rather wide waste-filled valleys.

The impressive High Sierra, which is the most prominent feature of this unit, has closely folded limestone ridges in the north and very elongated ridges in the south, cut through by some major rivers forming canyons. The typical karst morphology is found in many places.

Clastic and carbonate sediments, mainly of Lower Cretaceous and Triassic age, occupy extensive areas of the Sierra, with less extensive areas of Tertiary rhyolitic lavas, breccias, and tuffs. Unconsolidated fluvial and lacustrine sediments of Recent age occur with some frequency in the lower valley and foothill regions. Relatively small areas of calcareous shales and sandstones appear with crystalline limestone in the central area.

The dominant soil-forming parent materials of the steep mountainous terrain are limestone and related calcareous rocks. However, there are many undulating to rolling narrow ridges and plateaus included in this map unit, and here the main soil-forming parent materials appear to be a loess-like mixture. Desertic aeolian drift dominates in the north, true periglacial loess and rhyolitic volcanic ash in the centre, and intermediate to basic volcanic ash in the south.

A4. SIERRA MADRE DEL SUR SYSTEM

This unit includes the complex mountainous region south of the neovolcanic plateau where North American north-south trend lines interlock with the east-west trend lines of Central America and the Caribbean.

Most of the unit is rugged and broken country. The Sierra Madre del Sur forms much of Mexico's southern coast. It contains the important Balsas-Mexcala basin, which has an altitude of less than 700 m, while the surrounding mountain ranges can reach 3 500 m.

On the basin's southern flank are some of the most strongly dissected mountains in Mexico. They rise directly from the Pacific Ocean or from a narrow coastal plain to the rim of the upland at about 3 000 m. In the east the graben of the isthmus of Tehuantepec forms a clear boundary with the Central American mountain ranges.

Paleozoic metamorphic rocks, including extensive areas of gneiss and schist with smaller areas of phyllite, often mixed with intrusive rocks (both acid and basic), dominate in the coastal sector along the whole length of the map unit. The eastern flank is formed principally of carbonate sediments, usually Cretaceous. Clastic sediments also occur among the limestones; these are Lower Cenozoic sediments built up of the erosion products of pre-Tertiary rocks, and they contain interbedded basaltic and andesitic rocks.

Soils derived directly from gneiss, schist, phyllite, basaltic and andesitic lavas and tuffs, shales (usually calcareous), sandstones (locally arkosic), siltstones and mudstones (almost invariably calcareous) and limestone occur in this lithologically complex map unit.

A5. CENTRAL AMERICAN RANGES

This unit comprises the Chiapas-Guatemala-Honduras highlands which are separated from the Sierra Madre del Sur system by the graben of the isthmus of Tehuantepec. The Maya mountains in British Honduras are also included.

On the northwest there is a rather narrow coastal plain with some dune formation along the Pacific Ocean from which the Sierra Madre rises steeply. A chain of volcanoes surmounts the range. In and around the mountains and volcanic cones are intermontane basins.

The Sierra Madre is separated by the Grijalva depression from another range, the Sierra de Norte de Chiapas. From here the area descends to the Petén lowlands and Yucatán. The most impressive feature of this region is probably the Sierra de los Cuchumatanes, an elevated horst rising to a height of more than 3 800 m. The summits of this 60-km long block are smoothly rolling with characteristic karst morphology. Around the margins are deep canyons.

The northeastern part of the Chiapas-Guatemala-Honduras highland is, in essence, a highly dissected upland plateau, about 1 500 m high in the northwest, sloping down toward the east and southwest. The ranges are rather short, steep, and rugged, separated by intermontane basins.

Between the mouth of the Río Ulua and the Gulf of Fonseca lies the Honduras depression. The ranges west of it reach 2 800 m but toward the east the summits are lower.

The northeastern part of this sector forms the Central American (nonvolcanic) uplands, identified as soil region A8 in Chapter 5. The southern area is a volcanic region. Its boundaries with the sub-units in the north are indistinct geographically. The whole area is over 2 000 m in height, essentially a plateau, with summits of over 3 600 m in the west, and to the east a second series of plateaus between 600 and 1 800 m, with many volcanic cones.

The valley of the Lempa in El Salvador is 180 km long and runs parallel to the coast. In the south it is bounded by a double chain of volcanoes: an outer line comprising the most active volcanoes of El Salvador and an inner line of lower, dormant volcanoes. The plateau between the two chains is densely populated. This volcanic region is included in the Central American volcanic highlands as soil region A10b.

The Maya mountains, adjacent to the start of the Chiapas-Guatemala-Honduras mountain range in British Honduras, have steep slopes to the east and north. The northeastern end, at an altitude between 650 and 850 m, forms an undulating upland plateau. The Maya mountains coincide with soil region A7.

Mesozoic metamorphic rocks similar to those of map unit A4 continue down into the northern end of A5, but most of the central and southern sections of A5 are occupied by Tertiary effusive rocks. These are mainly rhyolite but include areas of dacite and ignimbrite. Commonly these acid volcanic rocks are interlayered with basalt flows, ancient volcanic ash beds, breccia, sandstone, conglomerate, and clay. Further to the south, in Nicaragua, ignimbrite and tuffaceous sediments are frequent, while pyroclastics and basalt are common in southeastern Nicaragua. Cretaceous limestones and dolomite are widespread only along the northeastern flanks of this map unit. Paleozoic metamorphic rocks occur in Guatemala, Honduras, British Honduras, and Nicaragua. Intrusive rocks in the map unit are dominantly acidic (granite, granodiorite, and some diorite). Ultrabasic rocks, including considerable areas of serpentine, occur in Guatemala adjacent to the area of metamorphic rocks. Volcanic ash beds of Quaternary age, now weathered to clay, are fairly widespread in the central and southern sectors of this unit.

Many of the rocks listed are soil-forming, but volcanic ash minerals have certainly contributed to the soil mantle over much of this map unit.

A6. ISTHMIAN RANGES AND ADJACENT COASTAL PLAINS

This unit starts south of the Nicaragua-Costa Rica depression and is separated from Colombia by the Atrato valley. It consists mainly of northwest-southeast aligned ranges with their fringing lowlands.

Increasing in height from northwest to southeast, the backbone ranges of the isthmus are crowned by the four great Costa Rican volcanic cones of Poás (2 704 m), Barba (2 906 m), Irazú (3 432 m) and Turrialba (3 328 m), and the Panamanian peak of Chiriquí (3 480 m). Evidence of recent volcanic activity increases as one approaches the southeast.

Between the Central and Talamanca Cordilleras, running obliquely to the axis of Costa Rica, lies the well-populated central valley. This upland region consists of predominantly rugged mountains and hills. Besides the relatively large central valley there are numerous scattered small plains, mainly along the coast, and many small hilly islands.

In Panama, the Cordillera Central, the extension of the Cordillera Talamanca, forms an arch of rugged mountains convex to the Pacific. It runs to the

Cerro Trinidad and the numerous low hills and plains of the central isthmus of Panama, which is crossed by the Panama Canal. The height of the mountains diminishes from west to east (from about 3 000 to 1 000 m).

The Pacific slope of the isthmus consists of the remnants of parallel, somewhat rugged hills, which form the peninsulas of Nicoya, Osa and Azuero, and many small, mostly hilly, offshore islands. Small plains fringing the peninsulas are often marshy. On the Caribbean side the coastal plain is better developed in Costa Rica than in Panama.

The basement rocks of this map unit are volcanic rocks of Mesozoic age and are dominantly andesitic. In many areas these have been overlaid by Tertiary and later volcanic rocks which range from basic (basalt, basic andesite) to acidic (rhyolite, dacite) and by shallow-water marine clastic and carbonate sediments ranging from Upper Eocene to late Miocene. Syenite, granodiorite, and granite of Pliocene age are minor acid intrusive rocks, common only in certain localities, but basic intrusives are relatively common in the Pacific peninsula regions of Costa Rica. Unconsolidated Quaternary and Recent fluvial and lacustrine sediments occupy much of the lowland landscapes.

Most of the rocks named are soil-forming in some part of the map unit, but in the immediate vicinity of the Tertiary and younger volcanoes the chief parent material is volcanic ash.

B. Plateaus

B1.   Northern plateau

B2.   Mesa Central

B3.   Neovolcanic plateau

B1.   NORTHERN PLATEAU

This unit is the continuation of the basin and range province in the western United States between the Sierras Madre Oriental and Occidental. This desertic area is the largest of the physiographical units mapped.

The plateau has waste-filled basins at an average height of more than 1 300 m. The height varies greatly, indicating an arid peneplanation with each feature reaching its own base level.

Between Saltillo and Nazas are the cross ranges which form the east-west connexion between the Sierras Madre Oriental and Occidental. These ranges are lower than the High Sierra (A3), while the valleys are much broader. Throughout the unit there has been extensive sedimentation either in the form of aeolian deposits contributing to ranges of

sand dunes in the north, or in the form of great alluvial fans and desert screes deposited by the many rivers in the lower parts of the mesetas.

Acid effusive rocks (mainly rhyolitic lavas, breccias, and tuffs) underlie the western part of this plateau, while clastic sediments with island hills and small transverse ranges of carbonate sediments (mainly of Cretaceous age) are common in the central and eastern sectors.

The plateau has an arid environment and the soil mantle is built up mainly of desertic aeolian deposits mixed with coarse fluvial and fan detritus resulting from occasional flash flooding, and from fine lacustrine deposits. An important ingredient in the soil materials accumulating in the lowest areas are the crystals of soluble salts transported by capillarity and concentrated by evaporation. Many of the soils in the western sector of this map unit contain some volcanic glass.

B2.   MESA CENTRAL

This map unit is a continuation of the northern plateau described previously. It has been treated as a distinct unit because of the more pronounced drainage systems of the Lerma, Moctezuma, and Pánuco rivers.

The basin of Mexico contains the greatest urban concentration of the whole area under study. It is a relatively large basin plain with some ranges, and with low, hilly areas surrounded by higher peaks and interconnected basin plains. The earlier name Anáhuac (" near the water ") possibly refers to the shallow lakes in the floor of the plain, several of which still existed at the time of the Spanish Conquest.

The basin of Toluca, west of the basin of Mexico but separated from it by mountains of over 3 000 m in height, is the most elevated of the intermontane basins. The basin of Jalisco, 1 600-1 700 m high, is the lowest. Several small volcanic cones, mud volcanoes and geysers occur in this basin.

This unit covers the same area as soil region A4 in Chapter 5, but it has been extended to the west and north to include the basins resembling the basin of Mexico. It also includes the Aguascalientes valley.

Effusive rocks, both acidic and basic, are common in this map unit. In the northwest and north, acidic rocks predominate, and the proportion of flow basalt and basaltic breccia and tuff increases toward the south and east. Clastic sediments and a few island hills of carbonate sediments occur throughout the map unit. However, soils formed from these rocks are far less frequent than those developed from Quaternary and Recent unconsolidated drift deposits, including some periglacial loess and moraine materials (east), desertic aeolian drift (north and northwest), fluvial and alluvial fan materials, and lacustrine beds (centre and southwest). Volcanic ash materials have contributed to the building up of most soils in the unit.

B3. NEOVOLCANIC PLATEAU

This plateau extends from south of Lake Chapala and the Tepic coast across the waist of Mexico to Orizaba in the east, and includes also the isolated Tuxtla mountains. Together with the Tuxtla mountains, the B3 unit is more than 850 km long. Along the southern rim of the plateau lies the Sierra Volcanica Transversal or Cordillera Néo-Volcanica, following a line of crustal weakness where volcanic activity still occurs.

The high plateau contains a broad spectrum of volcanic products: ash cones and lapilli of all sizes, basalt flows, rhyolites, and andesites — very deep deposits covering large areas on which much erosion has taken place. Over the ash-filled basins rise a great number of volcanoes, almost all extinct and in various stages of erosion. The most important are the Nevado de Colima (4 300 m), Popocatepetl (5 440 m), Ixtaccihuatl (5 290 m), Citlaltepetl or Pico de Orizaba (5 595 m), and the Cofre de Perote.

The Tuxtla mountains are a detached part of the neovolcanic plateau. Although lower, they are the highest mountains (about 2 000 m) on the north Atlantic coast south of Labrador. The rocks of this map unit are predominantly volcanic. Basic andesitic materials (flows, tuffs and breccias) are common, as are basalt flows and scoria cones. They are chiefly Miocene to Recent in age. Local areas of rhyolite and dacite are less in evidence and may represent an earlier phase in the volcanic activity that built up the plateau.

Volcanic ash forms deep unconsolidated beds over large areas of the plateau. The older beds are commonly weathered to clay and may be partially consolidated. The subaerial ash has been redistributed after each eruptive phase. Mudflow and lahar deposits are of local importance, and there are many examples of ephemeral lake and pond deposits formed by streams overloaded with volcanic ash. Volcanic ash is clearly the chief soil-forming parent material in this map unit.

C. Depressions

The Nicaragua-Costa Rica depression is the only one large enough to be distinguished on the physiographical map. It is a broad belt of flat to mode-rately dissected plain, up to 100 m in height, running diagonally in Central America from the Gulf of Fonseca in the northwest to the Caribbean coastal plain in Costa Rica in the southeast. It comprises the two great lakes of Nicaragua, Lago de Nicaragua and Lago de Managua, and the valley of the Río San Juan forming the boundary between Nicaragua and Costa Rica.

Although a distinct physiographical unit, it still lies within the volcanic areas in units A5 and A6. In fact, the Lago de Nicaragua itself has three volcanoes higher than 1 300 m, while the Momotombo (1 260 m) borders the Lago de Managua. These volcanoes, with all others in the region, belong to the Cordillera de los Marrabios.

Resorted admixtures of different kinds of volcanic ash (mainly andesitic and basaltic in nature) form the bulk of the lacustrine and fluvial deposits occupying the lowest flat land of the Nicaragua-Costa Rica depression. Undulating and rolling landscapes are usually covered with subaerial ash beds; in many of these the primary volcanic minerals are now weathered to clay.

D. Plains

D1. Gulf of California plain
D2. Gulf of Mexico coastal plain
D3. Yucatán peninsula
D4. Caribbean coastal plain

D1. GULF OF CALIFORNIA PLAIN

This unit lies between the Baja California peninsula and the Buried Ranges and consists of the Colorado delta and the desertic coastal plain of Sonora and Sinaloa-Nayarit.

The Gulf of California once extended as far as the Salton sea; into this the Colorado river built its delta. At present only a little water reaches the Gulf because most of it is used for irrigation in the Imperial valley. Sand is blown out of the delta, forming sand dunes in the Gran Desierto, which forms the northern extension of the Sonoran desert. The boundary with Baja California is sharp, but with the Buried Ranges it is indistinct. The plain varies considerably in width, from 10 to as much as 80 km. Most of the area is a flat plain of less than 100 m in height but containing numerous hills and hillocks, outliers of the Sierra Madre Occidental.

The deltas of the Yaqui, Mayo and Fuerte rivers include coastal marshes which are now transformed by irrigation into rich wheat, rice and cotton areas. Along the Sinaloa-Nayarit coast a score of rivers descend from the Sierra, and their contiguous deltas form a continuous low marshy coast.

The outliers of the Sierra Madre Occidental included in this map unit are mainly clastic consolidated sediments with some smaller outcrops of lacustrine and littoral sediments. These are the chief soil-forming parent materials in the area.

D2. GULF OF MEXICO COASTAL PLAIN

This unit stretches for more than 1 000 km, from the border with the United States at the mouth of the Rio Grande around the Gulf of Mexico to the base of the Yucatán peninsula. In the north it also includes a wide zone of foothills of the Sierra Madre Oriental.

The upper courses of the rivers crossing the northern part of the unit have a north-south alignment marking the outer folds of the Sierra Madre, but farther south a series of parallel east-west running rivers flowing to the Gulf divide the coastal plain into rectangular subregions.

The foothills in the northern sector are formed mainly from carbonate sediments. In the vicinity of the Tuxtla volcanoes, and again westward from Vera Cruz toward Orizaba, volcanic materials are common. In the southern and eastern sectors the plain is almost exclusively built up from fluvial sediments of varying ages. All of these are important soil-forming parent materials.

D3. YUCATÁN PENINSULA

This is a low, broad peninsula whose base is probably a block-faulted uplifted segment of the stable platform underlying the Gulf of Mexico, and on this base shallow-water limestones and coral reef debris have been accumulating since the Pliocene. Cumulative and probably steady emergence of this peninsula has exposed a sequence of limestones of successively younger age; the oldest are to be found at the base of the peninsula, and the youngest around the periphery and at the tip. In the oldest exposed members of the sequence the original crust has become disrupted (mainly as the result of activity by tree roots over the ages) and a more varied landscape is in process of formation as stream patterns develop in the softer limestone beneath the crust. Elsewhere, the landscape is of subdued undulating to flattish relief. The only permanent surface water is to be found in the few broad shallow depressions and in solution pits, but at a depth of 25 m and more there appear to be abundant reservoirs of fresh water.

This physiographical unit has been enlarged to include also the Petén lowlands of Guatemala, largely occupied by limestones and unconsolidated old fluvial sediments. The soils are formed directly from limestone only in the Petén sector and at the base of the Yucatán peninsula. Elsewhere the soils have been formed from whatever shallow-water coastal drift materials happened to lie on the hard crust immediately prior to uplift, supplemented by aeolian accumulation over the ages. During one of the periods of uplift the sea must have contained a large proportion of volcanic ash in suspension; after uplift this gave rise to red clay soils which still show traces of their volcanic origin.

D4. CARIBBEAN COASTAL PLAIN

This plain bordering the Caribbean sea is much smaller in extent than the coastal plain bordering the Gulf of Mexico. It is only in Nicaragua that it covers an appreciable area. The plain of eastern Nicaragua is for the most part less than 100 m high and consists of a broad flat belt with some scattered rolling areas. Hills of more than 150 m occur mainly as isolated features.

In the north of the D4 region there are intermittent strips of mangrove forests, lagoons and sandbars, coastal swamps and terraces. In southeastern Costa Rica and in Panama the plain is narrow and composed of continuous beaches backed by a low terrace.

Fluvial and coastal lacustrine sediments occupy most of this map unit and are the main soil-forming parent materials.

Caribbean islands

Hundreds of large and small islands stretch over more than 3 000 km from the Yucatán peninsula to the Venezuelan offshore islands. They include the Greater Antilles, between Yucatán and the Anegada passage to Grenada, and the continental islands including Barbados and the Venezuelan offshore islands. In this region there are also the Bahamas, which are covered in the Soil Map of North America (Volume II), and the island of Trinidad, the soil mapping units of which are listed in the Soil Map of South America (Volume IV).

Because of their relatively small size, most of the islands cannot be distinguished on the small-scale maps (1 : 20 000 000) used in the text, and only the islands of Cuba, Hispaniola, Jamaica and Puerto Rico, all belonging to the Greater Antilles and covering more than 90 percent of the land area of the Caribbean, are treated in some detail here.

The physiographical units distinguished in the Greater Antilles are marked on the map by a figure, preceded by a letter denoting the island (E, Cuba; F, Hispaniola; G, Jamaica; and H, Puerto Rico).

Cuba is about 1 300 km long and has a maximum width of 200 km. It has more relatively flat lowland than any of the other islands in the Greater Antilles.

Three comparatively small regions of mountain ranges, totalling less than 25 percent of the area, become progressively higher from west to east.

The first is the Sierra de los Organos, forming the western part of the Cordillera de Guaniguanico (E1). It rises to about 700 m and contains many karst phenomena. The second mountainous region is the Alturas de Trinidad Sancti-Spíritus (E2), where the peaks surpass 1 000 m.

The Sierra Maestra (E3) forms the western part of the most rugged mountain complex of Cuba. South and west of the Guantánamo valley, this range rises to an altitude of 1 960 m at the Pico Real. East of Guantánamo and south of the Sierra de Nipe the Baracoa region (E4) consists of rugged, deeply dissected mountain ranges and a few patches of flat land. Very steep cliffs separate both this region and the Sierra Maestra from the sea.

The Sierra de Nipe (E5) is an altiplano with an altitude of over 1 000 m, surrounded by lower hills where karstification has formed many caverns and underground holes.

The remaining three quarters of Cuba (E6) is principally composed of plains with gentle slopes formed on slightly dissected terraces.

Carbonate sediments are perhaps the most common rocks in Cuba; some are of Upper Jurassic age, and some of Lower Cretaceous and of Miocene. Rock types include limestone, marl, dolomite, conglomerate and some clastic sediments. The Lower Cretaceous carbonate rocks occur mixed with lavas and tuffs in eastern Cuba, often in proximity to clastic consolidated sediments. Effusive rocks (andesite, basalt, and related tuffs) occupy quite small areas in the north, but intrusive rocks are much more varied and more widely distributed. Basic intrusive rocks are of much greater extent and importance than acid intrusive rocks, which are restricted to relatively small areas. Metamorphic rocks (schist, phyllite, marble, quartzite and shale) form the greater part of the Isle of Pines and appear again in western Cuba and in small areas in eastern Cuba. Quaternary unconsolidated sediments cover most of the plains and coastal lowlands.

In Tertiary times Cuba would have been represented by a chain of islands. Subsequent regression of the sea level left the island hills joined by a platform of Tertiary sediments. Where these consisted of crystalline limestone, the erosion products from the adjacent high land (present as impurities in the limestone) have a considerable influence on the soil pattern. Most of the rock types mentioned are soil-forming.

Hispaniola is separated from Cuba by the Windward passage. Its physiography is much more complex than that of Cuba. A series of east-west rugged mountain ranges are separated by deep troughs. The mountains are usually deeply dissected.

The Cordillera Septentrional (F1) in the Dominican Republic exceeds 700 m in some places. It consists of dissected mountains with some high plateaus, and is bordered by a discontinuous narrow coastal plain in the north and the Valle del Cibao (F2) in the south.

The mountainous backbone (F3) of the island is formed by the Massif du Nord in Haiti and the Cordillera Central, Sierra de Yamasá and Cordillera Oriental in the Dominican Republic. The Massif is a complex of rugged, deeply dissected ranges and many relatively large intermontane valleys. Altitude varies from the nearly 3 200 m of the Pico Duarte to less than 100 m at other points.

Flanking the central mountain ranges in the south are a series of ridges and some prominent parallel valleys (F4). The Enriquillo basin and the Plaine de Cul-de-Sac form a deep depression, the bottom of which lies about 30 m below sea level. It contains two salt lakes.

The Massifs de la Hotte and de la Selle and the Sierra del Bahoruco form the southern mountains (F5) with peaks exceeding 2 000 m.

In the southeast of the island the plain along the Caribbean Sea (F6) is a mainly flat region consisting of older marine terraces and recent alluvial desposits.

Jamaica is dominated by the Blue mountains (G1) in the east (Blue mountain peak, 2 256 m), and a rugged white limestone plateau (G2) of very broken character, reaching 1 158 m, which occupies two thirds of the island. This plateau terminates in steep slopes dropping to strips of level coastal land (G3) in the west and south. These plains are extensive in some areas of the south, notably the Liguanea plain which covers 342 sq km.

Puerto Rico is dominated by an axial mountain range, the Cordillera Central (H1) reaching over 1 100 m in the El Yunque. The rainy northern slopes are deeply dissected by many rivers which have formed narrow valleys and sharp ridges. The main crest of the Cordillera is only about 15 km from the south coast. The drier southern slopes are much less dissected.

On the northern side behind a few discontinuous lowland areas lies a region of rolling to hilly terraces (H2), and the mountains begin abruptly south of these. The northwest has a karstic landscape.

The southern plains are discontinuous and usually very narrow (H3).

Puerto Rico is built mainly from effusive rocks ranging from Cretaceous to Eocene. They are principally andesitic pyroclastics, predominantly tuffs. Serpentine of Cretaceous age occupies a small area in the southwest, and acid intrusive rocks (granodiorites, quartz-diorite, diorite, and some gabbro) occur in the centre and east. Recent sediments include alluvial deposits and organic residues accumulating in swamps and marshes. Limestones occur along the northern and southern flanks of the island. Most of these rocks and unconsolidated sediments are soil-forming parent materials.

Other Caribbean islands include the Bahamas, the Cayman islands, the Swan islands, the Virgin islands, and the group called the Lesser Antilles. Most of the Bahamas are composed of limestone and littoral detritus resting on hard coral limestone. The soils are formed mainly from the unconsolidated calcareous fragments and organic debris.

The Cayman and Swan islands south of Cuba are similar in composition to the Bahamas, but the Virgin islands are composed largely of igneous and metamorphic rocks, including pyroclastics, volcanic breccias, and agglomerates.

LESSER ANTILLES

This group extends from Sombrero in the north to Grenada in the south, a long curving arc of small islands. Some are "low," formed mainly from coral rock overlain by coral detritus and calcareous sand, and some are "high," dominated by one or more volcanic peaks. The low coral islands lie to the east of the high islands, representing an arc of older volcanic peaks capped by Cenozoic limestone and younger coral formations. The younger western islands still have many active volcanoes. Rocks include effusive types (andesite, basalt, dacite, rhyolite) with sometimes a considerable area of tuffs and agglomerates, ash beds, mudflow and lahar deposits. On some of the high islands, limestones and marls cover the lower flanks of the older volcanic rocks.

A line of "continental" islands, extending from Barbados in the northeast to Aruba in the west, represents remnants of an ancient coastal range that once paralleled the north Venezuelan Andes. In Barbados there are exposures of marine sediments (including radiolarian earths) which are soil-forming in the Scotland district. Elsewhere the island is covered with coral limestone. Tobago is formed partly of acid and basic intrusive rocks, schists, and coral limestone.

Nueva Esparta island off the Venezuelan coast is formed chiefly of pre-Silurian metamorphic rocks. Metamorphic rocks also occur in Aruba, Curaçao, and Bonaire, but limestone covers much of the landscape of low relief.

Summary

The main points evident from this resumé of the geologic aspects of the Mexico and Central America region are:

- There are almost no very old land surfaces.
- Acid intrusive rocks and sedimentary rocks are relatively little distributed.
- There are very few ultrabasic rocks.
- Acid effusive rocks and their associated tuffs and agglomerates are widespread.
- Crystalline limestones occur throughout the map region.
- In some areas the landscape is blanketed by beds of subaerial volcanic ash.
- Large areas are covered by desert detritus and aeolian deposits.

In terms of soil genesis, one would therefore expect the soil assemblage to show:

- Very few Ferralsols.
- Limited distribution of Podzols. Strongly podsolized soils are equally scarce.
- Rather widespread Dystric Cambisols, Orthic Luvisols, and Acrisols.
- Widespread Vertisols and Rendzinas.
- Local areas of Andosols and andic intergrades to other soils.
- Large areas of Yermosols and Xerosols.

REFERENCES

ALLEN, PAUL H. *The rain forests of Golfo Dulce.* Gaines-
1956 ville, University of Florida Press.

ALPERT, LEO. *The climate of Hispaniola.* Worcester, Mass.,
1939 Clark University. (Thesis)

ALVAREZ, MANUEL. *Provincias fisiográficas de la República*
1961 *Mexicana.* Sociedad Geológica Mexicana. Boletín
Nº 2, Tomo 24.

BATALLA, ANGEL BASSOLS. *Recursos naturales (climas, agua,*
1967 *suelos).* México, Nuestro Tiempo.

BEINROTH, F.H. *An outline of the geology of Puerto Rico.*
1969 Rio Pedras, Puerto Rico, Agricultural Experiment Station. Bulletin No. 213.

BELTRAN, ENRIQUE. *Los recursos naturales del sureste y su*
1959 *aprovechamiento*, II Parte, Tomo 2. *Estudios particulares.* México, D.F., Instituto Mexicano de Recursos Naturales Renovables, A.C.

BENNETT, H.H. & ALLISON, R.V. *The soils of Cuba.* Wash-
1928 ington, D.C., Tropical Plant Research Foundation.

BIROT, P. *Les régions naturelles du globe.* Paris, Masson.
1970

BUTLAND, GILBERT J. *Latin America: a regional geography.*
1961 London, Longmans.

COMISIÓN DEL ATLAS DE PANAMÁ. *Atlas de Panamá.* Panamá,
1965 Dirección de Estadística y Censo.

DONDOLI, CÉSAR B. & TORRES, J. ALBERTO. *Estudio geoagro-*
1954 *nómico de la región oriental de la Meseta central.* San José, Ministerio de Agricultura e Industrias.

FAO. *Estudio de suelos del proyecto de irrigación de Rivas,*
1961 por R.F. Valencia. Roma.

FAO. *Survey of pine forests, Honduras.* Rome. FAO/SF:26
1968 HON 50. 2 vols.

FAO. *Enquêtes sur les terres et les eaux dans la plaine de Go-*
1968 *naives et le départment du nord-ouest. Rapport final.* Rome. FAO/SF:45 HAI 3.

FLORES MATA, G., JIMÉNEZ LOPEZ, J., MADRIGAL SÁNCHEZ,
1971 XAVIER, MONCAYO RUIZ, FRANCISCO & TAKAKI TAKAKI, FRANCISCO. *Tipos de vegetación de la República Mexicana.* México, Dirección de Agrología.

FRANCE. CENTRE NATIONAL DE LA RECHERCHE SCIENTIFIQUE.
1956 *Lexique stratigraphique international.* Vol. 5. *Amérique latine.* Paris.

GILL, T. *Tropical forests of the Caribbean.* Washington,
1931 D.C., Tropical Plant Research Foundation.

GRISEBACH, A.H.R. *Flora of the British West Indian Islands.*
1964 Weinheim, Cramer.

GUATEMALA. MINISTERIO DE AGRICULTURA. OBSERVATORIO
1964 NACIONAL I.A.N. *Atlas climatológica de Guatemala.*

HASTENRATH, S. Certain aspects of the three-dimensional dis-
1966 tribution of climate and vegetation belts in the mountains of Central America and southern Mexico. Geoecology of the mountainous regions of the tropical Americas. *Colloquium Geographicum, Proceedings of the Unesco Mexico Symposium, Universität Bonn.*

HOLDRIDGE, L.R. *Mapa ecológico de Guatemala.* Turrialba,
1959 Inter-American Institute of Agricultural Sciences.

HOLDRIDGE, L.R. *Mapa ecológico de Nicaragua.* Agencia para
1962 el Desarrollo Internacional del Gobierno de los Estados Unidos de América.

HOLDRIDGE, L.R. *Mapa ecológico de Honduras.* Washing-
1962 ton, D.C., Organización de los Estados Americanos.

HOLDRIDGE, L.R. *La vegetación de Costa Rica.* San José,
Dirección General de Estadística y Censos.

HOLDRIDGE, L.R. et al. *Atlas estadístico de Costa Rica. Los*
1950 *bosques de Guatemala.* Turrialba, Inter-American Institute of Agricultural Sciences.

HOLDRIDGE, L.R. *et al.* Report of an ecological survey of
1957 the Republic of Panama. *Caribb. Forester*, 17 : 91-110.

IMPERIAL COLLEGE OF TROPICAL AGRICULTURE, TRINIDAD. *Soil*
1958- *and land-use surveys.* 23 vols. Trinidad, Regional Re-
67 search Centre of the British Caribbean.

JAMES, PRESTON E. *Latin America.* New York, Odyssey
1942 Press.

LAMB, B. The forest of Darien. *Caribb. Forester*, 14: 1-2.
1953

LAUER, W. Problemas de la división fitogeográfica en Amé-
1966 rica Central. Geo-ecología de las regiones montañosas de las Américas tropicales. *Colloquium Geographicum, Proceedings of the Unesco Mexico Symposium, Universität Bonn.*

LEOPOLD, A.S. Vegetation zones of Mexico. *Ecology*, 31(4):
1950 507-518.

MARKS, H.B. Vegetation and soil relations in the lower Col-
1950 orado desert. *Ecology*, 31: 176.

MARTIN, PAUL S. *A biogeography of reptiles and amphibians*
1958 *in the Gomez Farios region, Tamaulipos, Mexico.* Ann Arbor, Mich., Museum of Zoology, University of Michigan.

MARTÍNEZ, MAXIMINO. *Las pináceas mexicanas.* 3ª ed. Ins-
1963 tituto de Biología, Universidad Nacional Autónoma.

MÉXICO. COMITÉ DE LA CARTA GEOLÓGICA DE MÉXICO. *Carta*
1960 *geológica de la República Mexicana.* 1 : 2 000 000.

MÉXICO. SECRETARÍA DE RECURSOS HIDRÁULICOS. *Datos de*
1962 *la región del Sureste.* Boletín Hidrológico Nº 18.

MIRANDA, F. & SHARP, A.J. Characteristics of the vegeta-
1950 tion in certain temperate regions of eastern Mexico. *Ecology*, 31: 313.

MIRANDA, F. Rasgos de la vegetación de la Cuenca del Río
1947 Balsas. *Rev. Soc. Méx. Hist. Nat.* 8: 95-114.

MIRANDA, F. & HERNÁNDEZ X., E. Los tipos de vegetación
1963 de México y su clasificación. *Bol. Soc. Méx.* 28: 29-179.

MÜLLER, C.H. Relations of the vegetations and climatic
1939 types in Nuevo Leon, Mexico. *Am. Midl. Natur.*, 31(3): 687-729.

MÜLLER, C.H. Vegetation and climate of Coahuila, Mexico.
1947 *Madroño*, 9(2): 35-57.

NICARAGUA. DEPARTAMENTO DE SUELOS Y USO DE LA TIERRA.
1969 *Suelos volcánicos de la región del Pacífico.* Managua.

ORGANIZACIÓN DE LOS ESTADOS AMERICANOS. *Mapa geoló-*
1966 *gico preliminar. República Dominicana*, 1: 250 000, pre-parado por Robert R. Blesch. Washington, D.C.

ORGANIZACIÓN DE LOS ESTADOS AMERICANOS. *Mapa geomor-*
1967 *fológico República Dominicana*, 1 : 500 000, preparado por Robert R. Blesch. Washington, D.C.

PANAMÁ. COMISIÓN DE REFORMA AGRARIA. *Mapa litológico*
1967 *aproximado de Panamá.* 1 : 500 000.

PERUSSET, M. *Le climat de Martinique.* Service Météorolo-gique du Groupe Antilles-Guyana.

RAISZ, ERWIN. *Map of the landforms of Mexico.* Prepared
1959 for the Geography Branch of the Office of Naval Research with inset map on physiographic provinces. Washington, D.C.

Los recursos naturales de Yucatán. *Boln Soc. Geogr. Esta-*
1950 *díst. Repúb. méx.*, 69(3).

ROBERTS, R.C. *Soil survey of Puerto Rico.* Washington,
1942 D.C., U.S. Department of Agriculture, Bureau of Plant Industry. Series 1936, No. 8.

ROBERTS, R.J. & ERVING, E.M. *Mineral deposits of Central*
1957 *America.* Washington, D.C., U.S. Deparment of the Interior. Geological Survey Bulletin 1034. (With a 1 : 1 000 000 geological map of Central America)

RZEDOWSKI, J. Vegetación del Estado de San Luis Potosí.
1965 *Act. Cient. Potos. Méx.*, 5(1-2): 1-291.

RZEDOWSKI, J. & MCVAUGH, R. La vegetación de la Nueva
1966 Galicia. *Contrib. Univ. Michigan Herb.*, 9(1) : 1-123.

SCHUCHERT, CH. *Historical geology of the Antillean-Carib-*
1935 *bean region.* London, Wiley.

SIMMONS, C. S. *et al. Clasificación de reconocimiento de los*
1958 *suelos de la República de Guatemala.* Guatemala, Instituto Agropecuario Nacional.

SMITH, EARL E. *The forests of Cuba.* Cambridge, Mass.,
1954 Maria Moors Cabot Foundation. Publication No. 2.

SORRE, MAX. *Mexique, Amérique central.* Tome 14, *Géogra-*
1928 *phie universelle.* Paris, Colin.

STANDLEY, P.C. & RECORD, S.J. *The forests and flora of Brit-*
1936 *ish Honduras.* Chicago, Ill., Field Museum of National History.

STANDLEY, P.C. & WILLIAMS, L.O. *Flora of Guatemala.* Chi-
1966 cago, Ill., Natural History Museum. Fieldiana, Botany, Vol. 24.

STRIKER, M.M. *Soils and land investigations in Panama.*
1952 Washington, D.C., Office of Foreign Agricultural Relations, U.S. Department of Agriculture.

TAYLOR, B.W. An outline of the vegetation of Nicaragua.
1963 *J. Ecol.,* 5(1) : 27-54.

TOSI, J.A. *Mapa ecológico de Costa Rica.* San José, Centro
1959 Científico Tropical.

UNIÓN PANAMERICANA. *Tenencia de la tierra y desarrollo*
1965 *socio-económico del sector agrícola de Guatemala.* Washington, D.C.

UNIÓN PANAMERICANA. *Reconocimiento y evaluación de los*
1967 *recursos naturales de la República Dominicana.* Washington, D.C.

UNIVERSIDAD NACIONAL AUTÓNOMA DE MÉXICO. *Datos cli-*
1969 *matológicos.* México, D.F.

U.S. AGENCY FOR INTERNATIONAL DEVELOPMENT. *National*
1965- *physical resources inventories of Costa Rica, El Salva-*
66 *dor, Honduras, Nicaragua and Panama.* Washington, D.C.

U.S. AGENCY FOR INTERNATIONAL DEVELOPMENT. *Maps of*
geology, surface configuration and rock types of El Sal-
vador 1 : 500 000 *and Honduras, Panama* 1 : 1 000 000.
Washington, D.C.

U.S. DEPARTMENT OF COMMERCE. *Census atlas maps of Latin*
1955 *America. Central America with map on land forms,*
1 : 4 000 000, by E. Raisz, 1953. Washington, D.C.

U.S. DEPARTMENT OF COMMERCE. *Greater Antilles, with map*
1956 *on land forms,* 1 : 4 000 000, by E. Raisz, 1953. Washington, D.C.

U.S. FOREST SERVICE. *The forests of Costa Rica.* Washing-
1943 ton, D.C.

U.S. WEATHER BUREAU. *Local climatological data, San Juan,*
1953 *Puerto Rico.* Washington, D.C.

VEENENBOS, J.S. *A soil and land capability survey of St. Maar-*
1955 *ten, St. Eustatius, and Saba.* Utrecht, Foundation for Scientific Research in Surinam and the Netherlands Antilles. Publication No. 11.

VIVÓ, T.A. & GÓMEZ, J.C. *Climatología de México.* Mé-
1946 xico, Instituto Panamericano de Geografía e Historia.

WAGNER, P. *Natural vegetation of Middle America.* Austin,
1964 Texas, University of Texas Press. Handbook of Middle American Indians, Vol. 1.

WEIL, R. *Die Geologie Mittelamerikas.* Beiträge zur Regio-
1961 nalen Geologie der Erde. Berlin, Gebrüder Borntraeger.

WEIL, R. *Die Geologie der Antillen.* Beiträge zur Regiona-
1966 len Geologie der Erde. Berlin, Gebrüder Borntraeger.

WOOD, HAROLD A. *Northern Haiti: land, land-use and settle-*
1963 *ment.* Toronto, University of Toronto Press.

WRIGHT, A.C.S. *Soils of the Yucatán peninsula.* United Na-
1968 tions Development Programme, Chapingo Project. (Mimeographed)

WRIGHT, A.C.S. *et al. Land in British Honduras.* London,
1959 HMSO.

5. THE SOILS OF MEXICO AND CENTRAL AMERICA

The legend of the Soil Map of Mexico and Central America consists of 301 map units in 259 different soil associations, each of which is composed of one or more soils occupying characteristic positions in the landscape. The sequence of their occurrence is related mainly to topography, geomorphology and lithology.

Each soil association is characterized by the dominant soil — the soil with the widest extension — and by associated soils and inclusions which occur in lesser extension. Fifty-six different dominant soils have been indicated on the map.

For convenience and brevity the soil associations have been listed in Table 3. The following information is given:

Map symbol. The map symbol of the dominant soil, followed by the number specifying the composition of the soil association, a second number indicating the textural class of the dominant soil, and a small letter indicating the slope class of the soil association. Textural class numbers are: (1) coarse, (2) medium, (3) fine. Slope class letters are (a) level to undulating, (b) rolling to hilly, (c) steeply dissected to mountainous.

Associated soils. Subdominant soils with an extension of more than 20 percent of the mapping unit.

Inclusions. Inclusions of important soils occupying less than 20 percent of the mapping unit.

Phase. Phases related to the presence of indurated layers, hard rock, salinity or alkalinity in the soil, or of cerrado vegetation.

Extension. An estimate of the area of the unit in thousands of hectares.

Occurrence. The countries of occurrence.

Information on vegetation and lithology related to the different soil associations can be abstracted from the vegetation and lithology sections of Chapter 4.

Distribution of major soils

On the continental land mass and most of the Caribbean islands mountainous or strongly dissected hilly landscapes are covered principally by lithic soil phases. In contrast, almost all areas of soil where lithic phases are not predominant are to be found either on lowland coastal plains or on some of the volcanic upland landscapes where rocky terrain is commonly mantled by volcanic ash.

Separation of the soils into major soil regions (Figure 6) begins with recognition of this division: on the one hand the soils of the highlands, on the other the soils of the peripheral fringe of coastal lowland, with adjacent foothills. Throughout the Pacific coast area the width of the lowland strip is relatively narrow, and the soils are derived almost entirely from the erosion products of the highlands. The lowland soils are so closely related to the highland soils above them that they are best considered as belonging with the particular adjacent highland soil region. The only lowland soil regions not showing intimate relationship with an adjacent highland region occur around the Gulf of Mexico, in the Yucatán peninsula, and around the Caribbean coast from southern British Honduras to Costa Rica. Many of the Caribbean islands have well-defined highland and lowland areas, but these cannot be shown on the small-scale map.

Within the highland region there are two distinctive areas where the soils show special relationships, caused by fine volcanic glass in the soil material. The northernmost of these "volcanic" soil subregions are commonly known as the neovolcanic uplands of Mexico. The southern volcanic subregion is often called the Central American volcanic highlands and extends as a continuous belt from the southern border of Mexico down the Pacific side of the continent to Costa Rica, with isolated fragments in northern Panama. The volcanic activity association with these subregions dates mainly from Quaternary time.

The nonvolcanic highlands of Central America are dominated principally by soils from crystalline limestones and related calcareous rocks, mixed with soils from volcanic tuffs and lavas of Tertiary age or older. The limestone subregion consisting of parallel folded ranges begins in eastern Chiapas, Mexico, and curves eastward into the Petén department of Guatemala. From there it continues along an arc with a northeasterly trend to reach the Caribbean sea in British Honduras; another branch reaches to the south and west, parallel to the Central American volcanic belt, to Panama. The narrower land mass between Costa Rica and the South American continent is considered as another subregion of the highland region, although the highlands here become a narrow, broken " isthmian " ridge, of relatively low elevation and with a climate more akin to that of a large Caribbean island than to the rest of continental Middle America.

As mentioned in the preceding chapter, the continental land mass of Middle America is little more than a narrow barrier between two of the world's largest oceanic weather systems. Consequently, the terrestrial environment is considerably affected by seasonal patterns of the maritime environment, and by Caribbean or Pacific air masses right across the land. Only in the northern part of Mexico is the continent sufficiently wide for truly continental weather patterns to develop. In north central and northwest Mexico the soils have developed under a desertic climatic regime, and this area must be regarded as a separate subregion of the highlands.

One other highland area needs to be mentioned: the area south of the neovolcanic uplands, extending across Mexico from Acapulco in the west to the Chiapas uplands in the east, with the Oaxaca upland basin near its centre. This subregion includes a large part of the geographic unit known as the Sierra Madre del Sur and part of the lower lying isthmus of Tehuantepec.

The Caribbean islands are a third major soil region, subject to maritime climatic conditions. In most of them the area of mountainous land dwarfs the extent of land of gentle relief. The majority are encircled by coral reefs. Some of the smaller islands are little more than slightly uplifted coral reef rock; even Cuba, the largest, is formed from a former chain of high islands that became linked by the uplifting of a common coral platform, similar to the coral platform of the Yucatán peninsula.

The regions and subregions shown in Figure 6 are described briefly below.

A. Highlands

A1. DESERTIC NORTHERN HIGHLANDS

This region represents the driest part of Middle America and is in effect a continuation of the system of desert ranges and basins of the North American continent. It is convenient to subdivide the Mexican desertic region into three subregions.

A1a. *Basins and ranges of north central Mexico*

This is an area of desert waste-filled basins at elevations between 1 200 and 1 700 m, separated or partially enclosed by abrupt rocky ranges rising 200 to 600 m above the basin floors.

The soils are Yermosols in the driest points of the desertic region and Xerosols in the slightly moister areas, with Kastanozems around the semiarid periphery. Almost all the soils are lithic in phase, and Lithosols dominate in the rocky ranges. Solonchaks and Solonetz occur in the lowest parts of some of the basins, and many of the basin Yermosols and Xerosols have strong petrocalcic horizons at shallow depth, especially around the margin of the basins. Deflated areas commonly show a " desert pavement " of polished gravel, or sheets of petrocalcic conglomerate may be exposed. Areas where windblown materials accumulate are characterized by Regosols.

A1b. *Buried ranges and desert plains of the northern Sierra Madre Occidental and the Sonora desertic lowlands*

An enormous mantle of desert waste moving westward from the desertic highlands toward the Gulf of California has partly buried the northern ranges of the Sierra Madre Occidental so that only the peaks of many of the ranges can now be seen. As the waste mantle converges on the lowlands it forms a vast sloping plain. Flash floods occur from time to time, and the soil is constantly disturbed by wind, so that the permanent plant cover is discontinuous — often restricted to patches of cactus, short tufty grass, creosote bush, and other small shrubs.

The dominant soils in this subregion are Yermosols and Regosols, with lithic Yermosols, lithic Xerosols, lithic Kastanozems and Lithosols on the buried ranges.

A1c. *Baja California peninsula*

This tilted fault block has an elevation of some 3 500 m in the north and descends consistently to about 600 m in the south. Granitic rocks occur in the north, but volcanic lavas and clastic rocks are more common in the centre and south. The environment is desertic. In many localities the plant cover is very sparse indeed.

The soils are mainly Yermosols and Regosols, with Lithosols, lithic Xerosols and lithic Kastanozems on the higher parts of the central ranges. At the southern tip of the peninsula, where rainfall is slightly higher, Kastanozems and lithic Chromic Luvisols may be found at lower elevations.

TABLE 3. – SOIL ASSOCIATIONS AND RELATED INFORMATION

Map symbol	Associated soils	Inclusions	Phase	Extension (1 000 ha)	Occurrence
Af19-1a	Ag Ap	Qa		191	British Honduras
Af20-2ab	Ag Lc			218	Mexico
Af21-2a	Ag Lo	Lf Gd		86	Guatemala
Af21-2a	Ag Lo	Lf Gd		10	British Honduras
Af22-2a	Fp Lf			18	Panama
Ag5-3ab	Ah Gh Fo	Jd		342	Panama
Ah5-2ab	Ao Lo	Ap I		781	Panama
Ah5-2ab	Ao Lo	Ap I		394	Costa Rica
Ah5-2ab	Ao Lo	Ap I		373	Honduras
Ah5-2b	Ao Lo	Ap I		541	Honduras
Ah6-3ab	Ap Wd	Gh		348	Nicaragua
Ah7-3c	Ao Fo Nd	I Jd	Lithic	409	Panama
Ah7-3c	Ao Fo Nd	I Jd	Lithic	362	Costa Rica
Ah8-2ab	Ap Bh Pl	I		20	British Honduras
Ah9-2bc	Af Bd Nd	I Je		1 845	Panama
Ah9-2bc	Af Bd Nd	I Je		150	Costa Rica
Ah9-2bc	Af Bd Nd	I Je		2 870	Nicaragua
Ah10-3bc		Be E I		12	Panama
Ah10-3bc		Be E I		43	Costa Rica
Ah10-3bc		Be E I		121	Honduras
Ao7-3b	Fo			237	Trinidad
Ao13-3c	I			114	Trinidad
Ao22-3a	Fp			77	Trinidad
Ao44-2bc	Be Lf	I E	Lithic	442	Guatemala
Ao44-2bc	Be Lf	I E	Lithic	879	Mexico
Ao47-3bc	I Nd	Th	Lithic	732	Mexico
Ao50-3ab	Bd	Ap		345	Costa Rica
Ao51-2bc	Bd Nd	E I Jd	Lithic	194	British Honduras
Ao52-2ab	Lc	Lf		797	Mexico
Ao52-2b	Lc	Lf		1 337	Mexico
Ao52-2bc	Lc	Lf		1 486	Honduras
Ao52-2bc	Lc	Lf		138	Guatemala
Ao52-3bc	Lc	Lf		63	Costa Rica
Ao53-3bc	Af I	Bd Jd Nd	Lithic	124	Costa Rica
Ao53-3bc	Af I	Bd Jd Nd	Lithic	740	Nicaragua
Ao53-3bc	Af I	Bd Jd Nd	Lithic	522	Honduras
Ao54-2ab	Ap	Gd I Wd		151	Cuba
Ao55-2bc	Lc Lo Nd	Bd I Lf		800	Cuba
Ao56-2bc	Bd I	Gh Je		120	Puerto Rico
Ao56-2bc	Bd I	Gh Je		6	Jamaica
Ao56-2bc	Bd I	Gh Je		116	Dominican Republic
Ao57-2ab	Lo Lp	Gh Jd		378	Guatemala
Ao57-2ab	Lo Lp	Gh Jd		162	Mexico
Ao58-2ab	Ap Qc	Gd Wd		977	Cuba
Ap5-2a	Wd	Gd		1 031	Nicaragua
Ap5-2a	Wd	Gd		205	Honduras
Bc4-3bc	E I Be	Je Vp	Lithic	178	Jamaica
Bc4-3bc	E I Be	Je Vp	Lithic	282	Guatemala
Bc4-3bc	E I Be	Je Vp	Lithic	741	Mexico
Bc4-3bc	E I Be	Je Vp	Lithic	242	British Honduras
Bc5-3bc	E I Ne	Je	Lithic	969	Dominican Republic
Bc5-3bc	E I Ne	Je	Lithic	1 338	Haiti
Bc10-3a	E Lc	I		51	Guadeloupe
Bc10-3a	E Lc	I	Lith./stony	3 665	Mexico
Bc10-3a	E Lc	I	Lith./stony	75	British Honduras
Bc12-2c	Be I	Re	Stony	109	Honduras
Bc12-2c	Be I	Re	Stony	234	El Salvador
Bc13-3a	G Lc We			276	Costa Rica
Bd8-3bc	Be I Nd	Je	Lithic	807	Dominican Republic
Bd8-3bc	Be I Nd	Je	Lithic	167	Haiti
Bd9-2b	Ao I			31	Panama
Bd19-3bc	Bh I Th	Pl	Lithic	126	Guatemala
Bd19-3bc	Bh I Th	Pl	Lithic	53	Mexico
Bd21-3bc	Bh		Lithic	79	Panama
Bd21-3bc	Bh		Lithic	86	Costa Rica
Bd25-3c	Ao I Nd	Je Lg	Lithic	1 033	Mexico
Bd26-2bc	Be I	Ao Re	Lithic	876	Nicaragua
Bd26-2bc	Be I	Ao Re	Lithic	2 001	Honduras
Bd26-2bc	Be I	Ao Re	Lithic	357	El Salvador
Bd26-2bc	Be I	Ao Re	Lithic	190	Guatemala
Bd27-3bc	Be I Lo	E	Lithic	325	Guatemala
Bd28-2bc	I Pl	Th	Lithic	655	Mexico
Be24-3ab	Lc E	I		13	Tobago
Be24-3ab	Lc E	I		902	Cuba
Be29-2/3c	I Re	Bv Vp Ne	Lith./stony	425	Nicaragua
Be29-2/3c	I Re	Bv Vp Ne	Lith./stony	248	Honduras
Be31-2a	Lc	Bd Ne		147	Costa Rica
Be32-3b	E I Lo	Je	Lithic	516	Guatemala
Be32-3bc	E I Lo	Je	Lithic	171	Honduras
Be32-3c	E I Lo	Je	Lithic	289	Guatemala
Be32-3c	E I Lo	Je	Lithic	34	British Honduras
Be33-3b	I Lc	Vp		6	Barbados
Be33-3b	I Lc	Vp		3	Windward islands
Be34-3bc	I Lc Ne	Bd Bc	Lithic	639	Cuba
Be35-2bc	Lc Vp	I Re		428	Mexico
Be36-3bc	E	Kl Lc		131	Cuba
Be36-3bc	E	Kl Lc		1 319	Mexico
Be37-3bc	E I Ne	Bd Je	Lithic	5	Antigua
Be37-3bc	E I Ne	Bd Je	Lithic	420	Dominican Republic
Be38-3bc	Ao Bd I	Je Vp		325	Puerto Rico
Be38-3bc	Ao Bd I	Je Vp		578	Mexico
Be39-2ab	Bv	Vp		882	Mexico
Be40-3b	Bv E	I		65	Dominican Republic
Be40-3b	Bv E	I		531	Cuba
Be40-3b	Bv E	I		13	Haiti
Be40-3b	Bv E	I		688	Mexico
Be41-3c	Bc E I	Je Vp		11	Antigua
Be46-2a	Ge	J		92	Mexico
Bh9-2bc	Ah Pl	I	Lithic	24	British Honduras
Bk5-2a	E I K	Vp		342	Mexico
Bk7-2bc	E Hl I	Vp	Lithic	1 180	Mexico
Bk8-2bc	E I Lc	Vp	Lithic	46	Cuba
Bk8-2bc	E I Lc	Vp	Lithic	2 809	Mexico
Bk9-3b	Bv I Lc	Vp Vc		28	Honduras
Bk9-3b	Bv I Lc	Vp Vc		218	Guatemala
Bv9-3ab	Lv Vp	Je		493	Mexico
Bv10-3a	Lv Vp	E Je		71	Nicaragua
Bv10-3ab	Lv Vp	E Je		238	British Honduras
Bv10-3ab	Lv Vp	E Je		8	Martinique
Bv10-3ab	Lv Vp	E Je		92	Cuba
Bv10-3ab	Lv Vp	E Je		104	Windward islands
Bv11-2a	Vp	Ne		1 277	Nicaragua
Bv11-2a	Vp	Ne		53	El Salvador
E2-3b	Bk I Vp	Lc		215	Guatemala
E2-3b	Bk I Vp	Lc		629	Mexico
E2-3b	Bk I Vp	Lc	Lithic	2 399	Mexico
E3-3bc	Hl I Lc	Re	Lithic	1 056	Mexico
E4-2a	Vp	Bv Ge Gm		228	British Honduras

TABLE 3. – SOIL ASSOCIATIONS AND RELATED INFORMATION

Map symbol	Associated soils	Inclusions	Phase	Extension (1 000 ha)	Occurrence
E5-3bc	Be I Lc	Vc Vp	Lithic	673	Mexico
E6-3bc	Bc Bv I	Vc Vp	Lithic	132	Puerto Rico
E6-3bc	Bc Bv I	Vc Vp	Lithic	279	British Honduras
E6-3bc	Bc Bv I	Vc Vp	Lithic	1 148	Guatemala
E6-3bc	Bc Bv I	Vc Vp	Lithic	12	Jamaica
E6-3bc	Bc Bv I	Vc Vp	Lithic	180	Mexico
E7-3a	Bv I Lc	Gm Vp	Lithic	17	Guadeloupe
E7-3a	Bv I Lc	Gm Vp	Lithic	6	Antigua
E7-3a	Bv I Lc	Gm Vp	Lithic	718	Cuba
E7-3a	Bv I Lc	Gm Vp	Lith./stony	1 278	Mexico
E8-3ab	Bv I Vp	Ge	Lithic	676	Mexico
E9-3ab	Ge Vp	I Sg		31	Barbados
E9-3ab	Ge Vp	I Sg		34	Guatemala
E9-3ab	Ge Vp	I Sg		2 449	Mexico
E10-3bc	Be I	Je	Lithic	134	Nicaragua
E10-3bc	Be I	Je	Lithic	1 256	Honduras
Fa3-2ab	Af Fr	Nd		436	Cuba
Fa5-2b	Fr			18	Puerto Rico
Fa7-2b	Bd Fr Nd	Ne		45	Dominican Republic
Fo27-3a	Ao Gd			152	Panama
Gc3-3a	Gm Je Zg	O Sg		339	Mexico
Gd22-2a	Ag	Ap		330	British Honduras
Ge18-2a	Be Lg Lp	Je Oe		977	Mexico
Ge19-2a	Gm Vp	We		47	Mexico
Ge19-2a	Gm Vp	We		68	British Honduras
Ge19-2a	Gm Vp	We		286	Guatemala
Ge20-2a	Re Vp	Tv		59	El Salvador
Ge20-2a	Re Vp	Tv		89	Guatemala
Ge20-2a	Re Vp	Tv		322	Mexico
Ge21-2a	Gm Je	Oe		94	Bahamas
Ge24-2a	Vp			77	Nicaragua
Gm10-2a	Je Lf	Oe		522	Mexico
Gm11-2a	Re Vp	Oe		392	Cuba
Gm11-2a	Re Vp	Oe		19	Dominican Republic
Gm11-2a	Re Vp	Oe		142	Mexico
Gm11-3a	Re Vp	Oe		3	British Honduras
Gm12-2a	Gp Lf	Ge Oe		218	Mexico
Gm12-3a	Gp Lf	Ge Oe		92	Cuba
Gm13-3a	Oe Rd	Od Je		348	Panama
Gm13-3a	Oe Rd	Od Je		253	Costa Rica
Gm13-3a	Oe Rd	Od Je		546	Nicaragua
Gm13-3a	Oe Rd	Od Je		317	Honduras
Gp2-3a	Gh Rd Wd	Od		115	Costa Rica
Gp2-3a	Gh Rd Wd	Od		692	Nicaragua
Hh10-2abc	Be Re I	Je		626	Mexico
Hl31-3ab	E I Vp			460	Mexico
I-ab				54	Curaçao
I-Bd-c				44	British Honduras
I-Be				22	Jamaica
I-Be-E-c				1 357	Mexico
I-E				1 089	Mexico
I-E-c				154	Cuba
I-E-Bc-a				481	Mexico
I-K-c				7 569	Mexico
I-K-E-c				3 712	Mexico
I-Ne-c				216	Dominican Republic
I-Ne-c				13	Windward islands
I-Ne-c				100	Jamaica
I-Re-Ne-bc				174	Mexico
I-X-c				2 133	Mexico
I-Xk-E-c				4 045	Mexico
I-Y-c				3 497	Mexico
Jc3-2a	Z		Saline	354	Mexico
Jd4-2a	Gd Wd	Gh Od		172	Costa Rica
Jd4-2a	Gd Wd	Gh Od		519	Honduras
Je1-3a	Jc			74	Trinidad
Je40-2a	Gh Gm	Lf Oe		177	Mexico
Je41-2a	Gh Re	Lf Oe		392	Mexico
Je42-2a	Gh Jd Re	Af Oe		9	Panama
Je42-2a	Gh Jd Re	Af Oe		181	Guatemala
Je42-2a	Gh Jd Re	Af Oe		348	Nicaragua
Je43-2a	Gh Lv Vp	Tv Vc		100	Dominican Republic
Je43-2a	Gh Lv Vp	Tv Vc		114	Puerto Rico
Je43-2a	Gh Lv Vp	Tv Vc		3	Windward islands
Je44-2a	Gh Je Vp	Jt We		3	Martinique
Je44-2a	Gh Je Vp	Jt We		11	Antigua
Je44-2a	Gh Je Vp	Jt We		14	Guadeloupe
Je44-2a	Gh Je Vp	Jt We		21	Puerto Rico
Je44-2a	Gh Je Vp	Jt We		178	Dominican Republic
Je44-2a	Gh Je Vp	Jt We		219	Jamaica
Je44-2a	Gh Je Vp	Jt We		248	Haiti
Kh18-2a	Kl Lc			502	Mexico
Kh21-2ab	Yl			92	Mexico
Kh21-2b	Yl			3 172	Mexico
Kh22-2b	E Kk Xl	S Vp	Lithic	593	Mexico
Kh22-2bc	E Kk Xl	S Vp	Lithic	4 270	Mexico
Kh23-2bc	I Kl Xl	Lc	Lithic	3 446	Mexico
Kk3-2b	Kh I	Xl	Petrocalcic	4 810	Mexico
Kk5-3a	V		Lithic	115	Mexico
Kk6-2ab	I	Xl	Lithic	395	Mexico
K17-2ab	I		Lithic	2 074	Mexico
K17-2bc	I		Lithic	6 276	Mexico
Kl15-2ab	Kk Re	E	Lithic	823	Mexico
Kl30-2bc	I Kh	Vp E	Lithic	7 194	Mexico
Kl32-2bc	Lv Re Vp	Be E	Lithic/ Petrocalcic	428	Mexico
Kl33-2bc	I Tv Vp	Re	Lithic	699	Mexico
Kl34-2ab	Lc Xl	I Re		980	Mexico
Kl34-2ab	Lc Xl	I Re	Saline	136	Mexico
Lc3-2a			Duripan	496	Mexico
Lc11-3ab	E Ne	Vp Bv	Lith./stony	1 440	Mexico
Lc25-3b	Kl	I		3 264	Mexico
Lc26-3ab	Be I			564	Mexico
Lc27-3bc	Be E Lo	Ne		44	Jamaica
Lc27-3bc	Be E Lo	Ne		98	Cuba
Lc28-3bc	Be Bk	Vc Vp		744	Mexico
Lc29-3bc	Be I	E		274	Mexico
Lc29-3bc	Be I	E		49	Guatemala
Lc30-3a	Bv E	Vp	Lithic	83	Puerto Rico
Lc30-3a	Bv E	Vp		3	Tobago
Lc30-3a	Bv E	Vp	Lithic	681	Dominican Republic
Lc30-3a	Bv E	Vp	Lithic	180	Haiti
Lc30-3ab	Bv E	Vp		52	Dominican Republic
Lc30-3ab	Bv E	Vp	Lithic	72	Jamaica
Lc30-3ab	Bv E	Vp	Lithic	194	Cuba
Lc31-3ab	Lv Tv Vp	Gm		31	Guatemala

TABLE 3. – SOIL ASSOCIATIONS AND RELATED INFORMATION

Map symbol	Associated soils	Inclusions	Phase	Extension (1 000 ha)	Occurrence	Map symbol	Associated soils	Inclusions	Phase	Extension (1 000 ha)	Occurrence
Lc32-3a	Be Vp	Je Vc		104	Panama	Nd33-3c	Bd I		Lithic	258	Dominican Republic
Lc32-3bc	Be Vp	Je Vc		106	Costa Rica	Nd33-3c	Bd I		Lithic	103	Haiti
Lc34-2b	Ne Tv			2 305	Mexico	Nd35-2ab	Ao I	Jd		91	Panama
Lc36-2ab	I	Be Vc		274	Panama	Nd35-2ab	Ao I	Jd		14	British Honduras
Lc36-2ab	I	Be Vc		138	Costa Rica	Nd36-3bc	Bc Lc Vp			77	Haiti
Lc36-3bc	I	Be Vc		241	Costa Rica	Nd36-3bc	Bc Lc Vp			443	Jamaica
Lc46-2b	Bc		Lith./stony	290	Costa Rica	Ne8-3b	Lc Lf Tv			1 301	Mexico
Lf19-2a	Lc Re	G		460	Mexico	Ne9-3ab	Bv Lc		Lithic	23	Haiti
Lf56-2a	Af Lp	Gh		726	Mexico	Ne9-3ab	Bv Lc		Lithic	36	Dominican Republic
Lf57-2a	Ao Be	I E		286	Mexico	Ne9-3ab	Bv Lc		Lithic	11	Antigua
Lf57-2bc	Ao Be	I E		956	Mexico	Ne9-3ab	Bv Lc		Lithic	6	Barbados
Lf58-2bc	Bd Th	Je	Lithic	445	Nicaragua	Ne9-3ab	Bv Lc		Lithic	1 738	Cuba
Lf58-2bc	Bd Th	Je	Lithic	40	Honduras	Ne21-2b	Be	I		72	Costa Rica
Lf58-2bc	Bd Th	Je	Lithic	427	Guatemala	Ne21-3abc	Be	I		9	Guatemala
Lg29-3a	Gm Je			94	Mexico	Ne21-3abc	Be	I		566	Mexico
Lg30-2a	Ge Vp We	Gm		313	Guatemala	Ne21-3bc	Be	I		38	El Salvador
Lg30-2a	Ge Vp We	Gm		363	Mexico	Ne21-3bc	Be	I		375	Guatemala
Lg31-2a	Gm	E		338	Guatemala	Ne22-2ab	Bv	I Re		325	El Salvador
Lg31-2a	Gm	E		333	Mexico	Ne22-2ab	Bv	I Re		126	Guatemala
Lo6-2/3ab	Lc Lf	Bv E		78	British Honduras	Ne22-2abc	Bv	I Re		384	El Salvador
Lo7-2ab	Be I Ne			111	Guatemala	Ne22-3ab	Bv	I Re		309	Nicaragua
Lo7-2ab	Be I Ne			183	Mexico	Ne23-3ab	Th	Bv		129	Costa Rica
Lo15-3ab	Ao			9	Guatemala	Ne24-2bc	Lc Tv	I	Lithic	64	El Salvador
Lo15-3ab	Ao			78	British Honduras	Ne24-3bc	Lc Tv	I	Lithic	62	Windward islands
Lo26-2bc	I Kl Lc	Lg Po		4 565	Mexico	Ne24-3bc	Lc Tv	I	Lithic	170	Haiti
Lo27-2bc	I Lg Nd			540	Mexico	Ne25-3bc	Tm	Tv		414	Guatemala
Lo28-2bc	I Kl Lc		Lithic	1 183	Mexico	Ne32-2ab	Tv			23	Costa Rica
Lo29-3b	Bc	Lf Ge		64	Guatemala	Od7-2a	Gh Jt Rd	S		9	El Salvador
Lo30-3bc	Ao I Lg	Bd	Lithic	127	Honduras	Od7-2a	Gh Jt Rd	S		143	Honduras
Lo30-3bc	Ao I Lg	Bd	Lithic	755	Guatemala	Od7-2a	Gh Jt Rd	S		101	Panama
Lo31-3bc	Bd Lg	Lf	Lithic	2 446	Mexico	Od7-3a	Gh Jt Rd	S		767	Cuba
Lo31-3bc	Bd Lg	Lf	Lithic	351	Cuba	Od7-3a	Gh Jt Rd	S		686	Panama
Lo32-3ab	Bd Nd		Lithic	212	Mexico	Od7-3a	Gh Jt Rd	S		37	Costa Rica
Lo33-3b	Be Bk Lc	E		110	Dominican Republic	Od7-3a	Gh Jt Rd	S		371	Nicaragua
Lo33-3b	Be Bk Lc	E		109	Haiti	Od7-3a	Gh Jt Rd	S		310	Honduras
Lo36-3bc	Bd Bv			212	Guatemala	Od7-3a	Gh Jt Rd	S		68	British Honduras
Lo37-2bc	Ao Tv			13	Tobago	Rc5-2c	Lc		Lithic	891	Mexico
Lo37-2bc	Ao Tv			59	Nicaragua	Rc7-2c	I Yh		Lithic	1 741	Mexico
Lo37-2bc	Ao Tv			995	Honduras	Rc8-2ab	I	Yh Yl	Lithic	65	Mexico
Lo37-2bc	Ao Tv			249	Guatemala	Rc16-2a	I			1 046	Bahamas
Lo37-3bc	Ao Tv			733	Honduras	Rd10-1a	Gd Od	Gh Jt S		224	Honduras
Lv3-3ab	Bv Tv Vp			236	Mexico	Rd10-1a	Gd Od	Gh Jt S		9	Guatemala
Lv4-3a	Bv Vp			339	Mexico	Rd11-2a	Gd Jt Wd	Od S		144	Costa Rica
Nd5-2b	Ao I			372	Panama	Rd11-2a	Gd Jt Wd	Od S		64	Panama
Nd5-3a	Ao I			152	Panama	Rd11-2a	Gd Jt Wd	Od S		104	Nicaragua
Nd5-3bc	Ao I			267	Haiti	Re12-1a	I X Y	S		747	Mexico
Nd5-3bc	Ao I			59	Cuba	Re12-1bc	I X Y	S	Lithic	1 691	Mexico
Nd26-3bc	Bd I Lo		Lithic	106	Costa Rica	Re12-1c	I X Y	S		676	Mexico
Nd26-3c	Bd I Lo		Lithic	304	Mexico	Re13-2a	X	I		398	Mexico
Nd29-3bc	Ah Ao I			86	Guadeloupe	Re20-2c	I K	Tv		1 104	Mexico
Nd29-3bc	Ah Ao I			47	Martinique	Re22-1ab	Kk Xl	Vc		156	Mexico
Nd29-3bc	Ah Ao I			58	Costa Rica	Re25-2a	Tv Vc	Je S Z		280	Mexico
Nd29-3bc	Ah Ao I			223	Panama	Re27-1a	Rc Yl			850	Mexico
Nd29-3bc	Ah Ao I			802	Nicaragua	Re28-1a	Tv	E I		413	Mexico
Nd30-3b	Ah Bd I			77	Haiti	Re29-1c	Tv	I		38	Mexico
Nd30-3bc	Ah Bd I			479	Panama	Re30-1b	I Tv			180	Mexico
Nd31-3ab	Ag Vc Wd	Gh		271	Panama	Re42-1c	I Th			20	Costa Rica
Nd32-3c	Ao I	Ah	Lithic	296	Panama	Re44-1c	I Ne Tv	Lc		31	Honduras
Nd33-3b	Bd I		Lithic	25	Puerto Rico						

TABLE 3. – SOIL ASSOCIATIONS AND RELATED INFORMATIÒN

Map symbol	Associated soils	Inclusions	Phase	Extension (1 000 ha)	Occurrence	Map symbol	Associated soils	Inclusions	Phase	Extension (1 000 ha)	Occurrence
Re44-1c	I Ne Tv	Lc		132	El Salvador	Vc22-2a	Vp	Ge Tv		58	Guatemala
Re54-1a	Tv Vc	Ge		12	El Salvador	Vp18-2a	Bv	Ne		29	Costa Rica
Re54-1a	Tv Vc	Ge		316	Guatemala	Vp18-2a	Bv	Ne		33	Nicaragua
Re55-1a	Gc Gm	Sg		552	Mexico	Vp21-3a	Yh	Vc		1 564	Mexico
Re56-1a	G Je	Oe S		29	Costa Rica	Vp27-3a	Be E Gc	Gm I		2 175	Mexico
Re56-1a	G Je	Oe S		9	El Salvador	Vp28-3ab	Be E I	Ge Hl Je		1 328	Mexico
Re56-1a	G Je	Oe S		37	Guatemala	Vp29-3b	E Kl	Ge Je		1 340	Mexico
Re56-1a	G Je	Oe S		124	Mexico	Vp30-3a	Lc Re Tv	Je S Z		325	Mexico
Re57-1a	Ge Gm Jt	Od S		61	British Honduras	Vp31-3a	Lc Re	Oe		567	Mexico
Re57-1a	Ge Gm Jt	Od S		425	Mexico	Vp32-3a	Lv Re	Je Lf		439	Dominican Republic
Re58-2a	Gh Od	Oe	Saline	416	Cuba	Vp32-3a	Lv Re	Je Lf		52	Puerto Rico
Re58-2a	Gh Od	Oe	Saline	569	Mexico	Vp32-3a	Lv Re	Je Lf		3	Haiti
						Vp32-3ab	Lv Re	Je Lf		888	Mexico
Th1-2b	L Tv	I		747	Mexico	Vp33-3a	Bk Re	Je		189	Mexico
Th6-2bc	I Tv	L		61	Guatemala	Vp34-3a	E Gm	I S		483	Guatemala
Th6-2c	I Tv	L		34	Guatemala	Vp34-3a	E Gm	I S		14	British Honduras
Th6-2c	I Tv	L		68	Mexico	Vp34-3a	E Gm	I S		968	Mexico
Th9-1c	I Tv	L Ne		146	Panama	Vp34-3a	E Gm	I S		1 767	Cuba
Th9-2bc	I Tv	L Ne		10	Guadeloupe	Vp35-3a	Ge We	E		224	Guatemala
Th9-2bc	I Tv	L Ne		16	Martinique	Vp36-2a	G Tv	Lc Lv		7	Windward islands
Th9-2bc	I Tv	L Ne		13	Windward islands	Vp36-2a	G Tv	Lc Lv		61	Guatemala
Th9-2c	I Tv	L Ne		3	Guatemala	Vp36-2a	G Tv	Lc Lv		29	El Salvador
Th9-2c	I Tv	L Ne		3	Mexico	Vp36-2a	G Tv	Lc Lv		86	Nicaragua
Th11-2c	Ao Tv	I Vp		310	Guatemala	Vp36-2a	G Tv	Lc Lv		12	Martinique
Th12-2c	Lc Tv Tm	G Vp		213	Costa Rica	Vp36-2a	G Tv	Lc Lv		186	Mexico
Tm5-2b	Tv	Vp		52	Guatemala	Vp37-2ab	Lc Ne Tv	Lv Vc		2 712	Mexico
Tm5-2b	Tv	Vp		168	Mexico	Vp38-3a	Hl Re	I Kl		723	Mexico
Tm6-2bc	Lc Tv	Nd		116	Nicaragua	Vp41-2a	Ge Je	Oe		49	Guatemala
Tm6-2bc	Lc Tv	Nd		442	Guatemala						
Tm6-2bc	Lc Tv	Nd		68	Mexico	Wd3-3a	G Lc	Lp		152	Panama
Tm6-2c	Lc Tv	Nd		106	El Salvador	Wd3-3a	G Lc	Lp		181	Costa Rica
Tm6-2c	Lc Tv	Nd		55	Guatemala	Wd3-3a	G Lc	Lp		13	Guatemala
Tm7-2b	I Ne Tv	Lc		53	Nicaragua	Wd3-3a	G Lc	Lp		3	British Honduras
Tm7-2bc	I Ne Tv	Lc		143	Nicaragua	We15-2a	Ge Lf Lp	Gm		91	Dominican Republic
To2-2bc	Bc I	Tv		575	Mexico	We15-3a	Ge Lf Lp	Gm		271	Dominican Republic
To4-2bc	Ao Bd Tv	I		279	Honduras	We17-3a	G Lc	Lp		266	Mexico
To5-2bc	Tv I Bd	Lc		3	Honduras	Wh2-2a	G Lg			218	Costa Rica
To5-2bc	Tv I Bd	Lc		41	El Salvador	Ws7-1a	J Vc	Re		330	Mexico
Tv13-1a	Re	E I		443	Mexico						
Tv14-2b	Re	I Ne		1 304	Mexico	Xh10-2bc	K Y	I	Lithic	708	Mexico
Tv15-1bc	Kl Lc	I Ne		5 733	Mexico	Xh36-2a			Hh	42	Curaçao
Tv15-2b	Kl Lc	I Ne		245	Mexico	Xk6-2ab	E Yk	I	Lithic/ petrocalcic	5 828	Mexico
Tv16-2bc	Lc	H Vp		1 593	Mexico	Xk7-2a	Re	E I	Lithic/ petrocalcic	1 012	Mexico
Tv17-2ab	Lc Vp	Je		558	Mexico	Xl10-2ab	I Y		Lithic	2 254	Mexico
Tv20-1bc	I Ne	Lc Th Vp		24	Martinique	Xl11-2abc	I K Y	S		1 130	Mexico
Tv20-1bc	I Ne	Lc Th Vp		86	Mexico	Xl12-2ab	I K Lc	G H		3 809	Mexico
Tv20-2bc	I Ne	Lc Th Vp		1 003	Mexico	Xl12-2ab	I K Lc	G H	Saline	192	Mexico
Tv21-2a	Gm Oe			342	Mexico						
Tv22-2bc	Re Th	I		1 930	Mexico	Y9-1/2b	I		Lithic	5 146	Mexico
Tv23-2ab	Lc Re	Vp		14	Costa Rica	Y10-2ab	Re	J I	Lithic	5 536	Mexico
Tv23-2ab	Lc Re	Vp		55	Panama	Yh9-2ab	I Rc Yk	Je		32	Mexico
Tv23-2bc	Lc Re	Vp		287	El Salvador	Yh12-2ab	I Re	E S	Lithic	2 375	Mexico
Tv24-2bc	I Ne			73	Panama	Yk9-2ab	E I	Re Yh Yl	Lithic	1 885	Mexico
Tv24-2bc	I Ne			20	Costa Rica	Yl5-1/2abc	Yk Rc			3 281	Mexico
Tv25-2bc	Ne Th	I		466	Costa Rica	Yl5-1/2abc	Yk Rc		Saline	156	Mexico
Tv26-2bc	I Lo Th	Pl		876	Mexico	Yl8-2abc	Je	Yk		9	Mexico
Tv27-2b	Ne Tm Vp	I		6	Costa Rica	Yl9-2abc	Re Yk			274	Mexico
Tv27-2b	Ne Tm Vp	I		496	Nicaragua	Yl12-2a	Kl	Rc Kk		637	Mexico
Tv28-2ab	Lo Th	Vp		75	Honduras	Yl14-2ab	Rc			4 458	Mexico
Tv29-2ab	Lc	Tm Lv		178	Guatemala	Yl14-2ab	Rc		Saline	198	Mexico
						Yl17-2a	Xl I		Lithic	649	Mexico
						Zo2-3a			Saline	242	Mexico

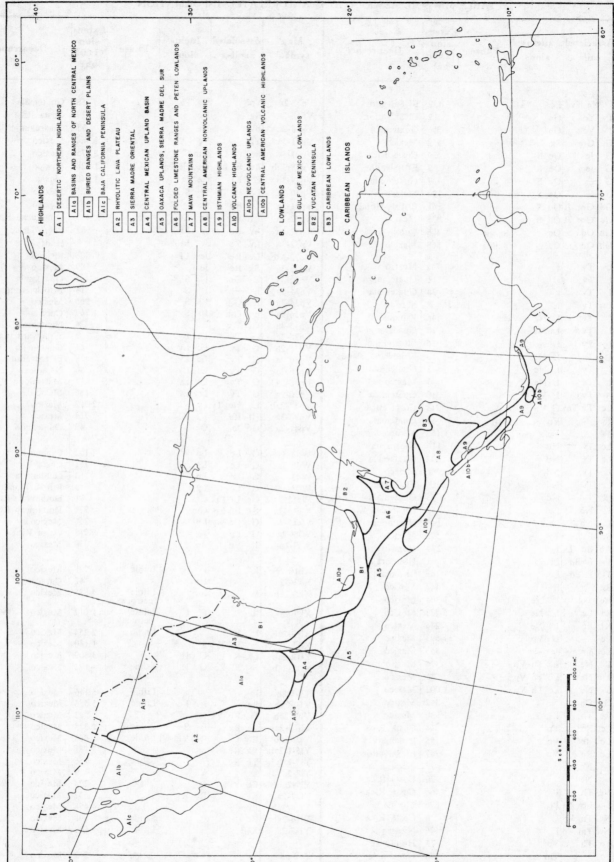

A. HIGHLANDS

A 1   DESERTIC NORTHERN HIGHLANDS
A 1a BASINS AND RANGES OF NORTH CENTRAL MEXICO
A 1b BURIED RANGES AND DESERT PLAINS
A 1c BAJA CALIFORNIA PENINSULA
A 2   RHYOLITIC LAVA PLATEAU
A 3   SIERRA MADRE ORIENTAL
A 4   CENTRAL MEXICAN UPLAND BASIN
A 5   OAXACA UPLANDS, SIERRA MADRE DEL SUR
A 6   FOLDED LIMESTONE RANGES AND PETEN LOWLANDS
A 7   MAYA MOUNTAINS
A 8   CENTRAL AMERICAN NONVOLCANIC UPLANDS
A 9   ISTHMIAN HIGHLANDS
A 10 VOLCANIC HIGHLANDS
A 10a NEOVOLCANIC UPLANDS
A 10b CENTRAL AMERICAN VOLCANIC HIGHLANDS

B. LOWLANDS

B 1   GULF OF MEXICO LOWLANDS
B 2   YUCATAN PENINSULA
B 3   CARIBBEAN LOWLANDS

C. CARIBBEAN ISLANDS

Scale

0   200   400   600   800   1000 Km.

Figure 6. Broad soil regions

A2. Rhyolitic lava plateau of the Sierra Madre Occidental

This region consists of a dissected high plateau contiguous with the western limits of region A1a. It also includes the adjacent coastal ranges and lowlands. The thick sheet of rhyolitic lava forming these dissected uplands extends southward for some 480 km, at an elevation ranging from 2 000-3 500 m.

Paleozoic and sedimentary rocks are exposed in the gorges and steep valley sides, and some basic andesitic lavas are exposed on the spurs of the range. There are indications of an ancient mantle of volcanic ash beneath the rhyolitic lavas, and in places these ash beds are exposed.

The eastern part of the rhyolitic plateau lies in very dry temperate and subtropical climates, and the common soils are Lithosols and lithic Kastanozems, with an open pine-oak-grassland vegetation. Descending westward toward warmer and moister climates near the Pacific Ocean, the soil assemblage becomes dominated first by lithic Orthic Luvisols, then by a complex pattern of lithic Dystric Nitosols (from basic volcanic rock), lithic Orthic Acrisols (from acidic volcanic rock and Paleozoic rock), occasional patches of Humic Andosols (from ancient volcanic ash), perhaps some Leptic or Orthic Podzols (from rare outcrops of siliceous sedimentary rock), and a large number of Lithosols.

Subdesertic semitropical climates in the north grade into very dry tropical climates in the south. Seasonally deciduous trees become more common in the forest, and lithic Chromic Luvisols are dominant. On the coastal foothills and plains Chromic Luvisols, Fluvisols, Regosols and Gleysols are present, with some Ferric Luvisols developed mainly on the wide interfluves of low coastal terraces.

A3. Sierra Madre Oriental

This mountain range forms the eastern boundary to subregion A1a and extends like a highly dissected mountain wall between the upland plateau of Central Mexico and the Gulf of Mexico lowlands. The dominant rocks are highly folded and faulted limestones, lutites, and related calcareous rocks of mainly Jurassic and Cretaceous age. They are strongly dissected by rivers flowing from the central plateau to the Gulf. The region is noted for spectacular landscapes.

In the western sector the soils include Kastanozems, Orthic Luvisols, and possibly some Luvic Phaeozems, all more or less lithic in phase, and Lithosols. At the northern end of the Sierra, where conditions are cooler and drier, only lithic Luvic Kastanozems and Lithosols have been reported.

From the west of the Sierra down to the Gulf lowlands the soil association is dominated by Lithosols, but includes Rendzinas, lithic Orthic Luvisols, lithic Eutric Cambisols, and some lithic Eutric Nitosols. A few isolated high plateaus along the crest of the range show occasional soils with profiles resembling Gleyic Luvisols and Leptic or Orthic Podzols, developed under pine woodland, from fine materials which may contain some loess from former mountain glaciers and ice fields.

In the central sector of the Sierra Madre Oriental all the slopes are steep and Lithosols, with associated Rendzinas and lithic Eutric Cambisols, are the main soils.

In the southern sector there has been sporadic accumulation of volcanic ash blown either from the neovolcanic plateau to the south or possibly from the isolated Tuxtla volcanic centre to the southwest. There are Humic and Ochric Andosols in addition to Lithosols. In a few places volcanic mudflows have spilled volcanic conglomerates through the mountain valleys to cover the inland sector of the Gulf lowlands. These conglomerates are normally cemented, and the soils consist mainly of shallow dark montmorillonitic clays, approximating to lithic Chromic Vertisols and lithic Vertic Cambisols.

Some of the most important soils of the region are the Eutric Fluvisols and Eutric Cambisols of the alluvial and colluvial deposits in the numerous narrow valleys. They are relatively insignificant in area, but their agricultural importance is very great.

A4. Central Mexican upland basin

This region, the heart of highland Mexico, consists of one large upland basin-plain, ringed around by higher peaks, and several interconnecting smaller basin-plains. This is the southern extension of the desertic basin system described under region A1a. The original vegetation, which has long disappeared, was probably pine-oak woodland and upland grassland. The mean elevation of the plain is about 850 m, and the surrounding peaks rise to between 4 500 and 5 750 m.

The soils of this region include Pellic Vertisols, Regosols, Vitric Andosols and Chromic Luvisols in the part of the basin bordering the neovolcanic uplands, with Kastanozems, Regosols and probably some Phaeozems becoming more common in the northern part of the plain. In the west, in a local "rainshadow" area of diminished rainfall, some lithic and petrocalcic Xerosols occur with Regosols. The old lake sediments in the centre of the plain principally give rise to Pellic Vertisols, while Eutric Fluvisols are common around the periphery.

A5. Oaxaca uplands, Sierra Madre del Sur, and adjacent Pacific coastal lowlands

This region comprises a complex series of dissected uplands and basins, with rivers flowing both north to the Gulf of Mexico and south or west to the Pacific Ocean. The rivers flowing south cut their way through a complex pattern of sedimentary rocks, including Paleozoic metasediments, while those flowing north dissect a series of Cretaceous limestone ranges and younger calcareous sedimentary rocks. The Oaxaca basin-plain represents one of the less dissected parts of the uplands, and is floored by Sub-recent and Recent alluvial and colluvial material from the surrounding ranges. Several small areas of ancient volcanic activity occur in the region, but lavas and clastic rocks tend to be local. No extensive areas of volcanic ash are reported. Along the Pacific coast there is a narrow strip of foothills and lowlands with a very dry tropical climate which is included within the region. The Gulf of Mexico lowlands, much wider than the Pacific lowlands, are shown as a separate region, B1.

The soils of the central uplands and basins include Pellic Vertisols, Eutric Gleysols, Eutric Fluvisols and Regosols in the basins proper; and lithic Calcic Cambisols and Chromic Luvisols (lithic and in part petrocalcic) on the hilly land and mountain slopes. Toward the Pacific coast lithic Eutric Cambisols, lithic Dystric Cambisols, lithic Dystric Nitosols and Lithosols have been reported from the coastal ranges under pine-oak forest at higher elevations and under semievergreen forest at lower elevations. Some areas of granitic rocks in the coastal ranges give rise to lithic Ferric Acrisols. The coastal plain has Vertisols, Gleyic and Chromic Luvisols, Gleysols, Fluvisols and Regosols, with lithic Haplic Phaeozems reported from the southwest coastal foothills near Tehuantepec.

A6. Folded limestone ranges and adjacent Petén lowlands

Hard, white, crystalline limestones of Cretaceous age form a wide arc of folded parallel ranges in this region. They swing eastward away from the main northwest-southeast trend of the older sedimentary rocks and finally curve northeast to partially envelop the isolated mass of the Maya mountain granites and Jurassic quartzite and shales in British Honduras. The highest elevations (over 1 500 m) occur near the start and finish of this limestone arc; in the centre the ranges become lower and more subdued as they pass through the Petén department of Guatemala.

The soils have yet to be studied thoroughly, but in the Mexican and Guatemalan sectors the dominant soils have been described as lithic Eutric Cambisols, lithic Chromic Cambisols, Rendzinas, and Lithosols. In British Honduras, lithic Chromic Cambisols occur, associated with hard pinkish limestones and dolomitic limestone. The Petén lowlands have Pellic and Chromic Vertisols, Eutric and Humic Gleysols, Orthic and Gleyic Luvisols, and some Planosols.

This region adjoins the Central American nonvolcanic highland in the south, along an indeterminate zone where the crystalline limestones are infolded with schists, sandstones and shales, and some Paleozoic granitic rocks. Along this marginal zone the soils are reported to be lithic Dystric Cambisols, lithic Orthic Luvisols and Lithosols, with Gleyic Luvisols and Leptic or Orthic Podzols appearing in some of the small upland plateaus of the granitic landscapes. Humic Acrisols have been reported on the outwash materials from this sector, at the head of the Usumacinta river. Rainfall is between 3 500 and 4 000 mm, and the forests are pine-cypress associations at higher elevations and mainly evergreen montane forests in the valleys. In the extreme southeastern corner serpentinized ultrabasic rocks occur mixed with limestone. Here the soil assemblage includes lithic Dystric Cambisols and Orthic Luvisols.

The eastern half of the Chiapas uplands has been included in this region because it is formed mainly from calcareous sedimentary rocks. It is an area of lower rainfall (900-1 500 mm) than the rest of the region. The soils include Chromic Luvisols, Vertisols, Calcic and Eutric Cambisols, and Rendzinas.

A7. Maya mountains

This region is relatively small in area but is distinct geologically. It consists of a mass of Jurassic quartzites, phyllitic shales, and sandstones, with a granitic batholithic core, block-faulted, uplifted some 1 000 m and tilted so that it presents very steep slopes to the east and south. The northern end forms a distinct upland plateau, underlain mainly by granitic rocks, which carries pine-oak forests and upland savanna. It appears to be an old erosion surface that has been above sea level for a very long time. The lower lying, down-tilted western and southern sectors of the horst are partially overlapped by the Cretaceous limestones of region A6.

The soils of the older land surfaces in the northeast corner include some which resemble Humic Acrisols, and others which are not unlike the Humic Cambisols of some of the old land surfaces of São Paulo,

Brazil. With these soils there are also Plinthic and Gleyic Luvisols. The steep slopes of the eastern part of the Maya mountains have lithic Dystric Cambisols, some lithic Humic Cambisols, lithic Orthic Acrisols (from sandstones and quartzites), and Lithosols. In the south and west the soils are mainly Rendzinas, lithic Eutric Cambisols, Chromic and Dystric Cambisols, and Lithosols.

A8. CENTRAL AMERICAN NONVOLCANIC UPLANDS

This region is a highly dissected upland plateau, with a maximum elevation of 1 500 m in the northwest, sloping down gradually toward the east and southeast. It commences in Guatemala, broadens to a maximum width of over 1 000 km in Honduras and loses its identity at an altitude of about 700 m in Nicaragua. The commonest rocks are Tertiary ignimbrites and rhyolitic tuffs (with some older granites, schists, shales and limestones in the northwest), and Tertiary andesitic tuffs and lavas in the south and east. Quaternary volcanic rocks are virtually absent. This upland region has been deeply carved by a complex network of streams and rivers emptying into the Caribbean, and few remnants of the original plateau remain.

The commonest soils of the mountainous landscapes are dark grey clay loams between 15 and 40 cm deep, grading into pale grey weathering ignimbrites and rhyolitic tuff. These have been frequently classified as Lithosols or Regosols, but since they have a clear cambic B horizon and are acid and of low nutrient status, they should be regarded rather as Dystric Cambisols. Lithic Eutric Cambisols and some Calcic Cambisols occur in the lower slopes of the drier intermontane valleys. To the south, in Nicaragua, the Tertiary tuffs in some areas contain a sufficiently high proportion of ferromagnesian minerals to permit the development of Dystric Nitosols, along with lithic Orthic Luvisols, lithic Dystric Cambisols, and some lithic Orthic Acrisols. Fluvisols, Planosols and Gleysols in the narrow valley floors throughout the region contribute to its agricultural production.

No related lowland coastal areas are included with this highland region.

A9. ISTHMIAN HIGHLANDS AND ADJACENT LOWLANDS

Almost the whole of Panama belongs to this region, which extends northward from the Colombian border across the Caribbean lowlands of Costa Rica to pass toward the Pacific along the trough occupied by Lake Nicaragua, and meets the southern end of the Central American volcanic highlands in Costa Rica.

A small area of the isthmian highlands consisting of Quaternary volcanic rocks belongs with the neighbouring region (A10b) to the north.

The commonest rocks are volcanic tuffs of Tertiary age. In general, they are more basic in nature than comparable rocks of region A8. The region consists essentially of a relatively narrow central mountain chain, with few inland plains and coastal lowlands restricted mainly to the embayed parts of the coastline. The narrowest part of the isthmus, where the Panama Canal crosses, is mainly rolling in relief, but the mountains begin again to the west and north of the canal and continue as a double chain to join the South American Andean foothills.

The Darien region of Panama has some interior valleys of considerable size, with Gleysols, Fluvisols and Gleyic Acrisols. Elsewhere the mountainous landscapes show lithic Orthic and lithic Humic Acrisols, and Dystric Nitosols. Orthic Acrisols, Ferric Acrisols and Dystric Nitosols are present on the lower lying hills of the Canal Zone. The soils of the related Pacific coastal lowlands include Planosols, Vertisols, Gleysols and Regosols. On the eastern sector of the Pacific lowlands, Chromic Luvisols are expected to be present.

A10. VOLCANIC HIGHLANDS

Under this heading are included the transverse volcanic highlands of Mexico (neovolcanic uplands) and the longitudinal belt of volcanic highlands flanking the Pacific Ocean from Guatemala to Costa Rica and reappearing again in western Panama.

A10a. *Neovolcanic uplands*

This subregion extends from Lake Chapala and the Tepic coast in the west, across the waist of Mexico to Jalapa and Orizaba in the east, and should also include the small isolated volcanic centre of Tuxtla on the shore of the Gulf of Mexico.

Essentially the region is a high plateau, with an average elevation of 2 800 m, but there are several large volcanoes rising more than 2 500 m above their plateau base. Some of these are intermittently active; in addition there are a large number of partially eroded, extinct volcanoes throughout the neovolcanic uplands.

The common rocks are Quaternary (or younger) lavas, tuffs, scorias and breccias. Varying amounts of fine volcanic ash of various mineral composition completely cover the hard rock in many localities. Buried soils are common.

The dominant soils are Andosols. Humic Andosols occur on older and more weathered volcanic ash beds in areas of higher rainfall, and there are smaller areas of Ochric Andosols where the rainfall is less abundant. Insufficient chemical data are available to determine whether Mollic Andosols are widespread on the old weathered ash beds of the humid to dry areas.

Most widespread of all are the Vitric Andosols, occurring where the ash beds are younger or less weathered. These are silty loam soils of great agricultural value, formerly referred to as Mexican Chernozems. In the drier areas they occur mixed with reddish clays that show the profile morphology of Chromic Luvisols. Such Chromic Luvisols are commonly formed from older, more weathered and consolidated volcanic ash in which most of the amorphous colloid formed during the initial weathering has been converted to halloysite. Many of these soils may still show a small proportion of amorphous colloid in addition to the predominant halloysite. This may account for the higher cation exchange capacity and higher alumina content compared with the more orthodox Chromic Luvisols of nonvolcanic landscapes. The topsoils also tend to be deeper and richer in organic carbon than typical Chromic Luvisols.

When volcanic glass weathers in an environment where calcium and magnesium are not continually removed by leaching, montmorillonitic clays are formed, and the soils are Pellic or Chromic Vertisols. Vertisols are fairly common in low positions on the neovolcanic plateau, and are frequent on the narrow strip of Pacific coastal lowlands.

A10b. *Central American volcanic highlands*

This subregion occurs as a relatively narrow longitudinal belt forming a Pacific mountain range extending southeast from near the southern limit of Mexico, through Guatemala and El Salvador to Nicaragua, thence to the central highlands of Costa Rica, to reappear as an isolated portion of the isthmian central ranges in Panama.

Within the Central American volcanic highlands the highest volcanoes are in the northwest; those to the southeast are lower. Almost all the rocks in this subregion are of Quaternary age or younger. There are over 66 distinct centres of volcanic activity in the subregion, 15 of them in active eruption since the turn of the century.

In Guatemala and El Salvador the volcanic highlands merge smoothly into region A8, but in Nicaragua they are separated by the low trough occupied by Lakes Nicaragua and Managua. In Costa Rica they form an interior range with drainage to both the Pacific and the Caribbean. Here and in Panama the volcanic highlands are surrounded by basic and acidic tuffs of the Tertiary rather than the Quaternary volcanism that is characteristic of this region.

There are frequently wide variations in the mineralogical composition of the different layers within the ash beds, and also differences in the age and stage of weathering of the ash, which make detailed soil maps complex.

Lithosols are not widespread in the Pacific coastal ranges despite the prevalence of steep slopes, because a thick mantle of volcanic ash can become stable on forested slopes and remain in place as long at the forest is undisturbed. Normal erosion by streams cutting their way headward may subsequently expose the underlying rock, but apart from this activity local occurrence of Lithosols is usually the result of rapid erosion following deforestation for agriculture.

The main soils in the subregion are similar to those of the neovolcanic plateau of Mexico, except that Humic Andosols are relatively more abundant, and Mollic Andosols become more common in the drier climatic regions. Vitric Andosols are more frequent on the coastal lowlands than on the uplands in most sectors. As in subregion A10a, the older and more weathered ash beds give rise to reddish (halloysitic) Chromic Luvisols, accompanied by Vertisols. Volcanic mudflow conglomerates give rise to Vertic Cambisols and Vertic Luvisols. Regosols are present in the highlands, mainly where the ejecta are very coarse pumice, cinders or scoria. Lithic Eutric Cambisols, lithic Orthic Luvisols and Lithosols occur on the Pacific slopes, particularly where there has been active stream down-cutting in the valleys.

In addition to Vertisols and Luvisols there are small but important areas of Fluvisols, Gleysols and Regosols in the Pacific coastal lowlands.

B. Lowlands

Important lowland areas occur in only three parts of Central America: bordering the Gulf of Mexico, the promontory of the Yucatán peninsula, and bordering the Caribbean coast from southern British Honduras to Panama.

B1. Gulf of Mexico lowlands

This region extends from the United States border at the mouth of the Rio Grande in a wide arc around the Gulf of Mexico, almost to the city of Campeche at the base of the Yucatán peninsula.

In the north there is a wide zone of foothills, ranging in height from 200 to 600 m, formed of limestone, lutite, and other calcareous rocks. The adjoining lowland is formed principally from calcareous alluvium and colluvium and dune sands. Toward the centre of the region the coastal lowlands are narrower, and volcanic materials from the highlands have covered much of the original alluvial landscape. Near the coast volcanic ash and local mudflow materials from the Tuxtla volcanic centres contribute to the formation of the lowland.

The soils of the Gulf of Mexico lowlands include Luvic and Calcic Kastanozems in the north, followed by Rendzinas, Luvic Phaeozems, Pellic Vertisols, Eutric Cambisols, Eutric Fluvisols, Eutric Gleysols and Regosols in central southern Tamaulipas. These continue southward and eastward until mudflow materials with lithic Vertic Cambisols and Vertic Luvisols dominate the lowland landscape. Vertisols, Gleysols and Regosols continue in the lowest position of the plain south of the city of Vera Cruz, but in the vicinity of the Tuxtla volcanoes, Vitric Andosols (in part lithic and duric), Eutric Fluvisols and Eutric Gleysols gradually dominate the lowlands. Beyond Coatzalcoalcos, a high sand dune barrier with Eutric Regosols marks the shoreline. Behind this barrier, Eutric and Humic Gleysols, Eutric Fluvisols and Histosols form a wide swampy lowland. The neighbouring foothills are carved in relatively soft Miocene sediments. On the ridges Ferric Luvisols are present with other soils that have the morphology of Acrisols but are perhaps too basic to fall in this category. In several localities the content of ferruginous minerals in the Miocene tuffs becomes high enough to give rise to Eutric and Dystric Nitosols. On the ancient Usumacinta flood plain sediments, under a cover of lowland savanna grasses, Planosols and Gleyic Luvisols are developed.

B2. YUCATÁN PENINSULA

As a geographic unit, the Yucatán peninsula has its roots deep in the Petén district of Guatemala and in the northern lowlands of British Honduras. The Mexican sector consists of the provinces of Campeche and Yucatán and the Territory of Quintana Roo.

The peninsula is a part of the Middle American coastline which shows evidence of cumulative emergence above the sea from late Cretaceous time onward. The earlier uplifting of the Maya mountains horst set the stage for a geomorphological process which thrust a finger of land into the sea and created a system of opposing currents between those of the Yucatán sea and those of the Gulf of Mexico. In the area of slack water between the two current systems, a shoal of coral fragments began to accumulate. Uplift in late Cretaceous time brought part of this shoal above sea level, and the uplift was repeated in the late Eocene and after.

An important feature of the geological process was the formation of a hard indurated crust in the shoal materials prior to the uplift. This carapace is resistant to weathering, and thus the successive emergent landscapes of the peninsula have retained their original inshore microtopography over a long period. On the part of the peninsula that emerged first, the hard carapace has become almost entirely shattered by the slow penetration of roots, allowing round karstic erosion processes to dissect the surface and permit a new cycle of soil formation. The principal soils are Rendzinas, Pellic Vertisols and Lithosols.

The part of the peninsula that emerged later — in late Miocene time — still has much of its protective carapace intact and is only weakly disrupted by tree roots. Here the soils are formed mainly from a thin layer of inshore coastal drift deposits that were in position on the carapace when the land was raised. At the time of uplift the sea was heavily infused with fine volcanic ash, and these ferruginous coastal sediments have given rise to conspicuous red soils. Their classification is not yet certain, but they fit best with Eutric Nitosols except for their very high calcium content.

Shallower red soils, sharing the landscape with the Nitosols, are regarded as lithic Chromic Luvisols. The shoal materials which emerged in Quaternary to Recent geologic periods still show very strong carapace formation, and the soils over the carapace are progressively less red and shallower. They are provisionally regarded as lithic Chromic Cambisols. The most recently emergent part of the peninsula has virtually no soil covering, but around the coast there are some coral sand dunes with Eutric and Calcaric Regosols, backed by a narrow zone of swampy land with Eutric Gleysols and some shallow Miocene Histosols.

Since all parts of the peninsula have a well-defined dry season there are no surface streams and no permanent surface water, except in some shallow depressions with cemented floors or floors that have become sealed with accumulations of fine clay. In these depressions there are small lagoons surrounded by Vertisols and Gleysols. Also present are Humic, Calcaric and Eutric Gleysols and Gleyic Solonetz. In the red soil zone there are Gleyic Luvisols as well.

B3. CARIBBEAN LOWLANDS

From the southern corner of British Honduras a narrow coastal lowland extends along the Guatemalan Caribbean coast and the north coast of Honduras, widening considerably along the east coast of Honduras, Nicaragua and Costa Rica, and narrowing again along the coast of Panama. It comprises a shoreline with shallow coastal water, very few natural deep-water harbours, an intermittent strip of coastal mangrove forest, lagoons and sandbars, areas of coastal swamp running inland, low coastal terraces, and a foothill zone of Tertiary rhyolitic and basic volcanic tuff or sandstones and shales easing gradually into the Central American upland region (A8).

The soils include Ferric Acrisols and Ferric and Orthic Luvisols in the north, and Orthic, Ferric and Plinthic Acrisols in the south, with Dystric Planosols, Thionic Fluvisols, and probably areas of Gleyic Solonetz.

C. Caribbean islands

All these islands are considered as a single major soil region, although even the smallest islands, where most of the rainfall is orographic, have areas of highland soils quite distinct from lowland soils; moreover the soils of the drier windward coasts are distinct from those of the moister leeward coasts.

Cuba, the largest of the Caribbean islands, is really a chain of small mountainous islands linked by a coral platform that was uplifted above the sea in Miocene time. The soils of this coral platform show considerable correlation with those of the Yucatán reef platform of equivalent age. Similar uplifted coral reef soils occur in Hispaniola, Puerto Rico and Jamaica. They are provisionally grouped with the Chromic Luvisols, Eutric Nitosols, Rendzinas and Lithosols.

In Cuba there are also extensive areas of Orthic Acrisols developed from schistose sedimentary rocks, Vertisols from alluvium, and Eutric and Dystric Cambisols, partly lithic in phase, on the sedimentary rocks of the Sierra Maestra in Oriente province. Nitosols formed on intrusive basic rocks and Acrisols on intrusive acid rocks, mainly in Oriente province, and there is a small area of Ferric and Gleyic Luvisols on some of the small upland plateaus of the Sierra Maestra. Deeply weathered reddish-purple soils from serpentine and related serpentinized ultrabasic rocks occur rather widely in Cuba. They appear again in the Dominican Republic, and in Puerto Rico where they were first described (Nipe clay). These are probably the only true Ferralsols appearing on the Soil Map of Mexico and Central America. They have been grouped provisionally with the Acric Ferralsols.

Hispaniola is mountainous, and the main soils are lithic Eutric and Chromic Cambisols, Rendzinas and Lithosols from the calcareous sediments and limestones, and lithic Dystric Cambisols and Lithosols where the mountains are formed from acid volcanic tuffs and quartz diorites. Areas of more basic tuffs give rise to Nitosols. Some parts of this island

have a dry climate with xerophytic thorny woodland, and in these areas lithic Calcic Cambisols have been described.

Jamaica has considerable areas of Chromic Luvisols, Rendzinas and Nitosols associated with limestone landscapes, in addition to lithic Eutric Cambisols, Lithosols and Luvisols from other sedimentary rocks. The smaller islands of the Antilles are usually either uplifted coral reef or the tops of volcanoes rising out of the sea. Among the volcanic islands, Dominica, Martinique and St. Vincent have areas of young soils from volcanic ash (Vitric Andosols) and soils from older ash beds (Humic and Mollic Andosols), as well as Vertisols and Vertic Luvisols at lower elevations. Grenada has considerable areas of red soils derived from weathered basic volcanic ash which are considered to be Dystric and Eutric Nitosols.

The islands of Antigua, Tobago and Barbados have no significant areas of volcanic rock. Eutric Cambisols, Luvisols, Rendzinas and Lithosols occur in Antigua; Tobago has Eutric Cambisols and Orthic Luvisols, with small areas of Dystric Cambisols derived from serpentine. Barbados is an emergent mountain top with concentric rings of coral limestone on which Rendzinas and Vertisols are developed. The highest (first emerged) of these platforms has Chromic Luvisols (mainly lithic phase) similar to those of Yucatán. The encircling reef rock is breached in the steeply sloping northeast sector of Barbados, and here Eutric Cambisols, Orthic Luvisols and Lithosols are formed from the exposed sedimentary rocks. Grand Cayman Island, Marie Galante and Barbuda are examples of low islands formed from uplifted coral. Much of the area consists of Lithosols and shallow Rendzinas, with pockets of somewhat deeper lithic Chromic Cambisols or lithic Chromic Luvisols.

REFERENCES

AGUILERA HERRERA, N. *Algunos suelos de la Meseta Tarasca:*
1961 *génesis y clasificación.* Chapingo, México, Escuela Nacional de Agricultura. Folleto Técnico Nº 1.

BALLOW, H.A. The Dutch Leeward islands. *Trop Agric.,*
1934 *Trin.,* 11: 317-320.

BENNETT, H.H. & ALLISON, R.V. *The soils of Cuba.* Wash-
1928 ington, D.C., Tropical Plant Research Foundation.

BLANCHE, D. & STEHLÉ, H. Enquêtes sur les sols de la Marti-
1949 nique. *Caribb. Bull.,* 3: 93-99.

CABRERA MESTRE, P. & GARCÍA, R. *Suelos de Cuba.* La
1946 Habana, Ministerio de Agricultura.

COMISIÓN DEL ATLAS DE PANAMÁ. *Atlas de Panamá.* Panamá,
1965 Dirección de Estadística y Censo.

48

COMITÉ INTERAMERICANO DE DESARROLLO AGRÍCOLA. *Inventa-*
1967 *rio de la información básica para la propagación del desar-*
rollo agrícola en la América Latina: República Domi-
nicana. Washington, D.C.

DONDOLI, C. & TORRES, J.A. *Estudio geoagronómico de la*
1954 *región oriental de la Meseta central.* San José, Ministerio de Agricultura e Industrias.

EL SALVADOR. MINISTERIO DE AGRICULTURA. DIRECCIÓN GENE-
1966 RAL DE INVESTIGACIONES AGRONÓMICAS. *Levantamiento*
general de suelos de la República de El Salvador. Santa
Tecla.

FAO. *Informe al Gobierno de la République Dominicana sobre*
1959 *la fertilidad de sus suelos,* por J. Kertleven. Roma.
Informe FAO/PAAT Nº 997.

FAO. *Informe al Gobierno de Nicaragua sobre génesis, clasifi-*
1966 *cación y levantamiento cartográfico de los suelos de*
Nicaragua, por N. Mikenberg. Roma. Informe FAO/
PAAT Nº 2021.

FAO. *Enquêtes sur les terres et les eaux dans la plaine des*
1968 *Gonaïves et le département du nord-ouest, Haiti.* Rome.
FAO/SF: 45 HAI-3.

FIPPIN, E.O. The soils of the Republic of Haiti, W.I. *Proc.*
1928 *1st Int. Congr. Soil Sci.,* 4: 270-275.

GUZMAN, L.E. *Farming and farmlands in Panama.* Chicago,
1956 Ill., University of Chicago, Department of Geography.
Research Paper No. 44.

HARDY, F. *Soil Foundation in the British Caribbean islands.*
1961 Turrialba, Inter-American Institute of Agricultural
Sciences.

HARDY, F. & RODRIGUEZ, G. *The agricultural soils of Mon-*
1949 *serrat.* Trinidad, Imperial College of Tropical Agriculture. Studies in West Indian Soils XI-1.

IMPERIAL COLLEGE OF TROPICAL AGRICULTURE, TRINIDAD.
1958- *Soil and land-use surveys of Jamaica.* Nos. 1, 4, 7, 8,
63 10, 12, 14. Trinidad, Regional Research Centre of the
British Caribbean.

IMPERIAL COLLEGE OF TROPICAL AGRICULTURE, TRINIDAD.
1958- *St. Vincent.* Land-Use Survey No. 3, 1958; *Grenada.*
66 Soil and Land-Use Survey No. 9, 1959; *St. Kitts and*
Nevis. Soil and Land-Use Survey No. 16, 1966; *Bar-*
bados. Soil and Land-Use Survey No. 18, 1966; *An-*
tigua and Barbuda. Soil and Land-Use Survey Nos.
19a and 19b, 1966; *St. Lucia.* Soil and Land-Use
Survey No. 20, 1966. Trinidad, Regional Research
Centre of the British Caribbean.

JARQUIN, G. et al. *Mapeo semidetallado de los suelos de la*
1965 *región del Pacífico de Nicaragua.* Managua, FAO/Minis-
terio de Agricultura.

KLINGE, H. Die Böden. El Salvador, Zentral-Amerika. *Neues*
1960 *Jb. Geol. Paläont. Mh.,* 9: 404-416.

MACÍAS VILLADA, M. Los estudios de los suelos en México
1963 y las unidades cartográficas. *Ingeniería hidrául. Méx.,*
17.

MACÍAS VILLADA, M. *Suelos de la República Mexicana.*
1964 México, D.F., Secretaría de Recursos Hidráulicos,
Dirección de Agrología.

MARTINI, J. Principales grandes grupos de suelos de Centro-
1967 América. *Fitotécnica latinoamericana,* 4(1-2).

MARTINI, J. et al. Forest soils of Darien province, Panama.
1960 *Trop. Woods,* 112: 28-29.

MARTINI, J.A. Algunos considéraciones sobre los suelos de
1969 América Central con referencia especial al desarrollo
del tropico húmido. *Fitotécnica latinoamericana,* 6:
127-147.

MATTHEWS, E.D. & GUZMAN, L.E. *The soils and agriculture*
1955 *of the "Llanos de Coclé."* Panamá, Ministerio de
Agricultura.

RICO, M. Soils of volcanic ash origin in El Salvador. *In*
1964 FAO. *World soil resources report* No. 14, p. 23-29. Doc-
ument, Meeting on the Classification and Correlation
of Soils from Volcanic Ash, Tokyo, Japan.

ROBERTS, R.C. *Soil survey of Puerto Rico.* Washington, D.C.,
1942 U.S. Department of Agriculture, Bureau of Plant Industry. Series 1936, No. 8.

RODRIGUEZ GÓMEZ, R. Los suelos de Drenaje Lento en la
1970 península de Yucatán. *Ingeniería hidrául. Méx.,* 24(1).

ROMNEY, D., ed. *Land in British Honduras.* London, HMSO.
1959 Colonial Office Research Publication No. 24.

SERVICIO INTERAMERICANO DE COOPERACIÓN AGRÍCOLA EN
1962 PANAMÁ. *Los suelos y las tierras de la provincia de*
Herrera. Panamá, Ministerio de Agricultura.

SIMMONS, C.S. et al. *Clasificación de reconocimiento de los*
1958 *suelos de la República de Guatemala.* Guatemala, Instituto Agropecuario Nacional.

TAMAYO, J.L. *Atlas geográfico general de México.* México,
1962 D.F., Instituto Mexicano de Investigaciones Económi-
cas.

THORP, J. *Soil survey (reconnaissance) of St. Croix island,*
1932 *Virgin islands.* Washington, D.C., U.S. Department of
Agriculture. Technical Bulletin No. 315.

U.S. AGENCY FOR INTERNATIONAL DEVELOPMENT. *Análisis re-*
1965 *gional de recursos físicos.* Nº 4. *Costa Rica.* Washington, D.C.

U.S. AGENCY FOR INTERNATIONAL DEVELOPMENT. *Inventario*
1966 *nacional de recursos físicos.* Nº 6. *Nicaragua.* Washington, D.C.

U.S. DEPARTMENT OF ECONOMIC AFFAIRS. NATURAL RE-
1969 SOURCES UNIT. *Survey of the natural resources of the*
Dominican Republic. Vol. 1, chapter 4, The soils of the
Dominican Republic. Vol. 3, Appendix, Soil description. Washington, D.C.

VALENCIA, R.F. et al. *Estudio de suelos del Proyecto de Irri-*
1961 *gación de Rivas.* Managua, FAO/Ministerio de Agricultura.

VARGAS VAGLIO, O. & TORRES, J.A. *Estudio preliminar de*
1958 *suelos de la región occidental de la Meseta central.* San
José, Costa Rica, Ministerio de Agricultura. Boletín
Técnico Nº 22.

VEALE, R.T. Characteristics of certain soils in the Domini-
1953 can Republic. *Proc. Soil Sci. Soc. Am.,* 17: 391-395.

VEENENBOS, J.A. *A soil and land capability survey of St. Maar-*
1955 *ten, St. Eustatius and Saba.* Utrecht, Foundation for
Scientific Research in Surinam and the Netherlands
Antilles. Publication No. 11.

WEBER, H. *Los páramos de Costa Rica y su concatenación*
1959 *fitogeográfica en los Andes suramericanos.* San José,
Costa Rica, Instituto Geográfico de Costa Rica.

WHITESIDE, E.P. & LEÓN OCHOA, H. *General report of the*
1961 *soils in the southern Papaloapan-Vera Cruz area, a por-*
tion of humid, tropical Mexico. East Lansing, Mich.,
University of Mexico.

WRIGHT, A.C.S. A New Zealand pedologist in the Carib-
1960 bean. I. Martinique. *Soil News, Wellington,* 2(5):
263-277.

WRIGHT, A.C.S. A New Zealand pedologist in the Carib-
1960 bean. II. Barbados. *Soil News, Wellington,* 2(6):
317-329.

6. LAND USE AND SOIL SUITABILITY

The land masses of Mexico, Central America and the Caribbean islands resemble nothing so much as a cornucopia, the broad end of the horn tipping slightly to the west so that the peninsula of Baja California spills over from the tilted rim, and the narrow end — somewhat irregular in shape but with convenient indentations for finger grips — curving away to the south and east.

The image of a horn of plenty could be misleading, although it fits the impressions of the earliest European navigators and the comments of the explorers, missionaries and geographers who followed them. To all these visitors the region was a populous one, a land that provided sustenance for settled peoples, in contrast with vast areas in North and South America that had only thin sprinklings of indigenous peoples of mainly nomadic habit.

If the earliest arrivals in the western hemisphere came by way of a land bridge from Asia, they must have found in the narrowing isthmus leading to South America many features tempting them to become permanent residents of the highland plains and valleys. For others who may have come from Africa, moving northward along the Caribbean coastal waters, the islands and the Central American eastern shores also presented many favourable features lacking along the coastline of northern South America. Probably the only land regarded as unattractive for settlement was the narrow strip of lowland between the coast and the interior foothills — a place of dense forests, rivers liable to sudden flooding, reptiles, insects and insect-borne diseases. This strip, moreover, presented a landscape where the majority of the soils were unsuited for the growing of traditional food crops. Indeed, what once may have existed as a no-man's land, separating the scattered Afro-Indian lowland coastal settlements from the populous Amerindian highland territories, for centuries continued to be largely unsettled until quite recent times. Only in the past few decades has modern agricultural technology been pitted against the somewhat inferior soils, adverse climatic factors, and the exuberant natural plant cover of this area.

Settlement in the eastern lowlands in pre-Columbian times was limited to the upper arc of the Gulf of Mexico, where volcanic soils extend from the highlands down to the eastern lowlands of the continent, and even here there are parts where agriculture is still in the pioneer stage. The Pacific lowlands, especially those adjacent to the volcanic highlands, became controlled by city states that were usually offshoots of earlier highland settlements, and were well established in pre-Columbian times. To this generalized picture of the land-use pattern one must add the scattered population of the desertic north and northwest. This was determined as in all desert areas by the reliability of water supplies. Archeological evidence suggests that quite large local populations developed in some favoured areas, devising techniques for exploiting subsurface waters, often of considerable natural salt content, in their efforts to survive. However, most of these desert dwellers had disappeared long before the Spanish Conquest.

The main areas of ancient Amerindian settlements were the warm temperate highlands and the subtropical high valleys, places where the soils were derived from volcanic ash or calcareous rocks, with either adequate rainfall or with permanent water from rivers, crater lakes or upland basin lakes. Little is known about the original food crops. The immigrants from the north must have reached the fertile warm temperate highlands of Mexico with only limited subsistence crops at their disposal, mostly squashes, beans, and small grains. The subsequent evolution of maize to the point where it became the staple food crop of the whole highland region was perhaps an inevitable development. On the other hand, the coastal Afro-Indian migrants from the south almost certainly depended on root crops such as cassava. Even when maize became generally available throughout the region it could not take the place of cassava as a dependable food crop for the lowlands because of the limited extent of suitable soils and the high rainfall and humidity. Even today, Amerindians in the Caribbean lowlands of British Honduras and Guatemala do not depend solely on maize, and plant considerable areas of cassava.

The general pattern of agriculture in pre-Columbian times displays a certain logic. For all peoples, highland and lowland alike, food crops had to be produced without hard-metal tools, and transported without draught animals or the wheel. Fire was the main agent for removal of the natural vegetation, and in areas not dry enough to support fire the trees, vines and shrubs had to be bruised and broken in advance so that they would dry out sufficiently when the rainy season passed. In other words, soils for planting had to be selected with an eye to the suitability of the plant cover for burning. Where possible, an Amerindian selects lithic soil phases on steep slopes for three logical reasons: the forest on a steep slope is usually composed of smaller trees which are easier to prepare for burning; the fire then ignites more readily and spreads more evenly; and, lastly, the soils are certain of adequate surface drainage during the rainy growing seasons.

Since the area cleared is sown not only with maize but with a whole range of other food crops (including bananas, plantains, pineapples, pepper, culinary herbs, climbing beans, and even some permanent trees such as coffee, citrus and cocoa), the ground is well covered in the rainy season and soil erosion is not as serious as usually claimed. Slight acceleration of natural erosion is inevitable with this type of farming, but helps to ensure that the soils never lack an admixture of fresh rock particles which release plant nutrients on weathering. Thus, fertility is regenerated when the land is cleared after three to six years' rest.

As long as there is an adequate area of land at his disposal, the Amerindian farmer remains skilled in the use of lithosolic soils. When rising population restricted to a limited land area forces the Amerindian to recultivate his lithosolic terrain at shorter and shorter intervals the traditional system of farming begins to break down and the soils become permanently damaged. Even when the population pressure becomes severe, however, the traditional system continues to be workable for a long time wherever soils are derived from limestones or volcanic ash.

Much has been written about the disastrous effects of this kind of farming on the erosion of landscapes, but there is no certain evidence in Central American volcanic ash or limestone soils that traditional Amerindian farming ever significantly altered the normal rate of erosion, even after the Spanish preempted many of the upland basins and plateaus for their own estates. Accelerated erosion caused by traditional Amerindian farming is a comparatively recent phenomenon, and reflects the need to settle within

reach of schools and markets, plus the markedly increased population growth following improved medical services and rural hygiene. Old habits die hard, and today there is still quite a large seminomadic population of Maya and Kekchi Indians exploring the uninhabited limestone ranges of the foothills of Guatemala and British Honduras, seeking new areas of lithosolic soils where they might settle for a generation or so.

The arrival of the Spanish conquerors did far more than drive the highland plateau farmers into the ranges and valleys. The introduction of draught animals and wheeled transport meant that crops would move more easily and extended the farmers' operations. Crops more tolerant of frost (such as potatoes and wheat) raised the range of agriculture beyond the 2 800 m altitude limit which was in force when maize was the only important food crop. The still later advent of upland rice is currently promoting a movement of Amerindian farmers down to lower altitudes, where rice and maize production are combined.

Agriculture in the Caribbean lowlands has always lagged behind that in the west. On the Pacific coast, lowland soils were in use for subsistence crops in pre-Columbian times, and later for estate agriculture and livestock farming. Little farming of any kind was attempted on the eastern lowlands until comparatively recently. The Pacific lowlands are much drier and have more fertile soils, enriched by the periodic deposition of fine volcanic ash. The cost and effort of clearing the xerophytic woodland and open deciduous forest on the west coast were far lighter than they were for the dense rainforest of the eastern lowlands. In addition, the farmer of the east coast normally has to face high installation and maintenance costs for drainage (and also needs occasional irrigation during the one or two months when rainfall is unreliable), and construction and upkeep of access roads are more costly. Over the last century the Caribbean lowlands have seen much agricultural effort, but they remain the only large area of undeveloped soils in the Central America, Mexico and Caribbean islands region.

For easy reference, the discussion of land use and suitability of the dominant soils is given here in alphabetical order of symbols.

A. Acrisols

Af. FERRIC ACRISOLS

Use. These soils appear on the map in a few localities along both the Pacific and Caribbean coasts, mainly in areas where there are low coastal terraces formed from Pleistocene alluvium. The soils are formed under tropical lowland forest and high rainfall, in areas remote from accumulation of volcanic ash. They are strongly acid, low to very low in plant nutrients, and are used as rough grazing land or for limited production of subsistence crops such as cassava, or for pineapple, cashew and rice.

Suitability. Under traditional methods of farming these soils cannot repay the farmer for the expense of liming, fertilizing, and draining. Without improvement, however, they barely yield adequate crops of rice, cassava, and pineapple to maintain the family.

Under improved farming systems, the initial cost of bringing these soils to the point where they can be made to yield pasture for beef cattle and adequate crops will be high. Pineapple is the cheapest crop to establish and maintain, but the total area of these soils in any one locality would be barely sufficient to support an economic local canning industry.

Ah. HUMIC ACRISOLS

Use. These soils are not widely used at present, except where they occur as the lithic phase (mainly on the mountain slopes of Costa Rica, Panama and Nicaragua) where they can produce subsistence crops in traditional systems of shifting cultivation.

Suitability. Under traditional systems the lithic phase of these soils are farmed in conjunction with adjacent alluvial and colluvial soils in valleys. Yields from maize are very low; from cassava, fair to low; upland rice, fair; beans and most other seasonal crops, low to very low. Abandoned cropping areas take a long time to regain fertility (10 to 15 years) and many areas are never used again. Symptoms of nitrogen, phosphate and potash deficiency are common. Nonlithic Humic Acrisols are not used by traditional farmers except as rough grazing land.

Under improved farming systems these soils present several problems: they require liming and they contain colloids which restrict the availability of phosphate and necessitate phosphatic fertilizers. Their natural supply of soil nitrogen is rapidly depleted, but nitrogen added as fertilizer is readily leached out by the high rainfall of the environment. Drainage is essential on landscapes of gentle relief, but erosion of drainage channels becomes excessive on slopes of five degrees and over. The soils are best developed under permanent pasture, directly after the forest cover is removed, with heavy dressings of lime and fertilizer to create conditions where legumes (such as kudzu and centrosema) can begin

to raise the nitrogen levels in the soil. Applications of granulated triple phosphate are needed two or three times a year.

Ao. ORTHIC ACRISOLS

Use. The Orthic Acrisols present fertility, drainage and erosion problems similar to those of the Humic Acrisols but in a lesser degree, and they are in more general use. They occur widely in southern Mexico, British Honduras, Guatemala, Honduras, and parts of Nicaragua and many of the Caribbean islands. Their present land-use pattern includes pasture, sugarcane, tobacco, pineapple, cashew, citrus, and subsistence crops, but in many areas the crops look poor and give low yields.

Suitability. Under traditional management, extensive cattle grazing is the only economic use on landscapes of gentle relief, but on the lithic phases of the mountainsides, moderate to poor yields of maize can be obtained with a 12-15 year recuperative cycle. Upland rice raised by traditional methods as a cash crop is growing in popularity in some areas.

Under improved management systems, the lithic phases are of little agricultural value, but on more gentle relief citrus, coffee and pineapple can be grown if erosion and drainage can be controlled by contour planting along the slopes. With adequate fertilizers and careful management, good dairy pastures are being developed on these soils in Cuba and elsewhere.

Ap. PLINTHIC ACRISOLS

Use. Restricted to relatively small areas of the Caribbean coastal lowlands from British Honduras southward, these soils are not yet in general agricultural use apart from extensive grazing on the natural savanna grasses.

Suitability. Under traditional systems these soils are unmanageable, apart from seasonal firing of the natural grassland to promote fresh grass growth for livestock.

Under improved management systems something could probably be done with these soils to make them suitable for rice production under irrigation. They are level to undulating and easy to clear of their natural vegetation (grass with scattered pines). They have a notably impervious subsoil and thus conserve irrigation water, and they occur in situations where water supplies are no problem. They are very acid and very low in plant nutrients, but physical conditions are not adverse for rice growing. Jute is grown on these soils in South America.

B. Cambisols

Bc. CHROMIC CAMBISOLS

Use. These soils occur mainly in southern Mexico, northern Guatemala, British Honduras and central Honduras, and in some of the Caribbean islands (for example, Hispaniola), in areas where the parent rocks are calcareous and contain volcanic minerals in the form of tuff. They are commonly found in the lithic phase and are widely used for subsistence crops grown by traditional systems.

Suitability. Under traditional systems they give moderate crops of maize and beans, fair yields of bananas, plantains and root crops. These traditional systems can be maintained with a resting period of five to eight years between crops on the lithic phases of these soils.

Under improved farm management systems the lithic phases can be profitably used for such tree crops as nutmeg, avocado, and to a lesser extent citrus, coffee and cocoa, in areas where labour is plentiful and inexpensive. Regular applications of phosphate are essential to maintain production because the soils contain enough ferrous iron and aluminium compounds to restrict the availability of soil phosphates. Nonclimbing leguminous cover crops should be grown beneath the trees.

Bd. DYSTRIC CAMBISOLS

Use. Found mainly in areas of siliceous rocks (such as granites, quartz diorites, quartz sandstones) in mountainous regions with a high to very high seasonal rainfall (3 500-5 000 mm), these soils occur chiefly in the lithic phase on the steep mountain slopes. They occur in southern Mexico, northern Guatemala, British Honduras, the Dominican Republic, Costa Rica and Panama, but are not intensively farmed.

Suitability. Under traditional systems these soils yield such poor crops that farmers seldom return for a second planting of maize. Some of the deeper colluvial soils found along the slope foot provide quite good crops of cassava and plantains.

Under improved systems, the steepness and ruggedness of the terrain and the prevailing shallowness of the soil, together with the low natural fertility, all combine to make these soils of little value. Of the commonly associated soils, usually Orthic Acrisols and Dystric Nitosols, only the latter are sometimes used for coffee and citrus orchards.

Be. EUTRIC CAMBISOLS

Use. Developed under subhumid and humid environmental conditions from mainly calcareous sedimentary rocks on hilly and steep land, the Eutric Cambisols of the region are used principally for tree crops such as cocoa, pastures and subsistence crops (maize and beans). They occur, mainly as lithic phases, in Mexico, Cuba, the Dominican Republic, Antigua, Barbados, Tobago, British Honduras, Guatemala and Honduras.

Suitability. Under traditional management Eutric Cambisols are among the most popular soils for maize, yielding adequate crops from the same area at intervals of only three to five years in most countries.

Under improved management they are usually suitable for tree crops and pastures. In the more humid localities they are often used successfully for cocoa and coffee, without recourse to fertilizers.

Bh. HUMIC CAMBISOLS

Use. These soils are scarcely represented in Central America and are not mapped in Mexico or the Caribbean islands. They appear only at higher elevations in British Honduras and near the Costa Rica-Panama border where the parent materials are granites and quartzites. They are very acid soils, usually containing high levels of free aluminium, and are not used for agriculture.

Bk. CALCIC CAMBISOLS

Use. These are chiefly known as extensive grazing soils in the subhumid mountainous areas formed from limestones, lutites and related calcareous rocks in central Mexico. Smaller areas of similar soils occur in Guatemala, Honduras, Cuba and the Dominican Republic, but in all localities lithic soil phases are dominant.

Suitability. Owing to marked seasonal dryness, traditional farmers can do little with these soils apart from grazing the natural grassland that comes when the xerophytic woodland has been destroyed. Improved farming methods are limited by lack of water for irrigation and the problems of distributing water over strongly rolling and hilly landscapes. The soils are generally rather shallow, even on the easier relief, and are highly erodable. They are, however, quite fertile; where seasonal rainfall is adequate and slopes permit, regular crops of maize can be grown by mechanized farming. Erosion control measures are essential for sustained yields.

53

Bv. Vertic Cambisols

Use. Vertic Cambisols occur mainly on the flanks of the volcanic highlands of Mexico and El Salvador where basic volcanic conglomerates (formed by lahars and mudflows) are giving rise to soils under mainly subhumid tropical conditions. They are fertile soils used for a wide variety of crops during the rainy season but tend to become rather dry and fissured in the subsoil during the dry months. Coffee is sometimes grown on the deeper soils, but lithic and duripan phases are generally left for pasture.

Suitability. Traditional farmers find little difficulty in growing subsistence crops on these soils.

Improved farming methods have been successfully applied to the growing of cotton and sugarcane, in addition to maize, sorghum, beans and rice.

E. Rendzinas

Use. Rendzinas derived from hard white crystalline limestones or from lutites and related calcareous rocks are common along the eastern flank of the Mexican highlands, continuing through the Petén sector of Guatemala into British Honduras and Honduras. Rendzinas from chalky marls and coral limestone are widespread in the Yucatán peninsula and also occur in Cuba, Haiti, the Dominican Republic, Puerto Rico, Jamaica, and many of the smaller Caribbean islands. They occur over a wide climatic range, from temperate to tropical and from semiarid to humid; consequently their land-use characteristics are varied. Rendzinas commonly occur in complex association with Lithosols and bare rock outcrops, and frequently occupy small pockets of shallow soil. In areas of adequate seasonal rainfall and temperatures Rendzinas were the preferred soils of the ancient Maya farmers for growing maize; today they are still highly prized for this purpose by Amerindian farmers.

Suitability. For traditional farmers these are highly satisfactory soils because they are fertile and well drained, can be used on a fairly quick rotation (three to five years), and their second-growth vegetation is easy to dispose of when the time comes for clearing the land again. Provided the rains start on time and rainfall is adequate during the growing season, yields that satisfy the traditional farmer are assured.

For farmers using improved techniques the Rendzinas are much less rewarding. The rocky and patchy nature of the soil either defeats mechanization or makes maintenance of equipment a costly item. Crop-ripening tends to be uneven, reflecting the patchiness of the soils. Most modern farmers on Rendzinas sooner or later abandon arable farming in favour of permanent grassland. In mountainous areas, where lithic Rendzinas and Lithosols predominate, modern methods find no application. The tree crop best suited to these soils in some districts appears to be the avocado. Sugarcane is grown as a plantation crop on Rendzinas formed from chalky limestones in northern British Honduras, and here a need for regular application of potash fertilizers is apparent.

F. Ferralsols

Fa. Acric Ferralsols

Use. Ferralsols as a group are uncommon throughout Central America, Mexico and the Caribbean islands. Significant areas occur only in Cuba, the Dominican Republic and Puerto Rico. Small areas occur as associate soils in Panama and perhaps Nicaragua. The Ferralsols of the islands are mainly derived from serpentinized ultrabasic rocks. They are deeply weathered soils, with a low calcium/magnesium ratio and very low availability of phosphate. Certain trace elements are often present in toxic amounts (nickel, chromium), while others are deficient. They are exceedingly infertile and are not in general use for agriculture.

Suitability. Acric Ferralsols are unsuited for farming by traditional methods, and so far have proved largely unsuited to farming by improved methods. Experiments in Cuba suggest that the modern farmer must virtually build up a new soil on the surface of the original one. This means very shallow working of the uppermost soil layers, heavy dressings of organic manures, and heavy liming and phosphate topdressing to establish shallow-rooting grasses. Reforestation with pines is also proving a slow and difficult process on Acric Ferralsols in Cuba.

G. Gleysols

Gleysols of varying kinds occur throughout the map region. Although they vary widely in chemical and physical properties, they all share one property that strongly influences their land use potential: poor drainage and excess of water in the subsoil during the greater part of the year.

Use. The commonest land uses are grazing and raising crops that can tolerate periods of excess water, such as rice. Where there are nearby urban markets, dairying is also common, and where the markets are strong enough to justify the expense of drainage improvements, vegetable and horticultural crops may be grown.

Suitability. Traditional farmers are able to utilize Gleysols of high and moderate fertility by digging a simple drainage system to lower the water table sufficiently so that crops such as rice, jute, sugarcane, bananas, Liberian coffee, and others adapted to seasonal wetness of the soil, can thrive. The trouble with traditional farming on these soils is often the failure to realize that drainage improvement of a small area is seldom effective if the surrounding farmers are not doing likewise and working to a master drainage plan. It is not the depth of a farmer's local drainage system that matters so much as the length of the outlet drain for the whole area. Comprehensive and efficient drainage systems are difficult to achieve under traditional management. Pastoral farming is common.

Improved management, on the other hand, can do a great deal with Gleysols to make them productive for a wide range of crops. Once the water table is brought under control, Eutric and Calcaric Gleysols seldom need more than occasional fertilizing, although Dystric and Humic Gleysols normally require regular amounts of nitrogenous, phosphatic and potassic fertilizers to maintain high yields. Humic Gleysols, occurring as associate soils in areas near the coast and usually dominated by Regosols or other kinds of Gleysols, are more difficult to farm. Problems of consolidation, shrinking, compaction and excess sodium salts frequently develop in these soils after a few years of farming. They are best used for extensive grazing until they have settled down under their new moisture regime. Subsequently they can be ploughed and used for sugarcane or vegetable crops.

H. Phaeozems

No extensive areas of Phaeozems have been reported in this map region. In Mexico, one small area of Luvic Phaeozems has been mapped in Tamaulipas state, and Haplic Phaeozems, mainly lithic in phase, are reported from the southwest coast of Oaxaca state. They are used mainly for rough grazing by traditional farmers.

I. Lithosols

Use. Lithosols are common throughout Central America and Mexico but usually occur as an associate of lithic phases of other soils. Map units dominated by Lithosols are found chiefly in Mexico in desert zones and along the flank of the Sierra Madre Oriental. In the desert areas the Lithosols are not used except for extensive grazing after rain. Elsewhere they are used where the rocks are fissured and can be readily penetrated by tree roots. In some places tree crops like citrus and coffee are grown on steep slopes of shattered rock with only the thinnest veneer of soil. Lithosols occur on flattish and undulating landscapes in Yucatán: here they consist of a coral limestone pavement with an indurated crust. The overlying soils are usually thin and stony.

Suitability. Traditional farmers use Lithosols with lithic phases of other soils for shifting cultivation, but even under humid tropical conditions the yields of maize are noticeably lower on the Lithosols than on the lithic phases of the dominant soils. Areas where Lithosols predominate are usually avoided by traditional farmers.

Improved management systems leave Lithosols severely alone, and in some enlightened cases afforestation or preservation of the existing natural plant cover is attempted.

J. Fluvisols

Use. Fluvisols appear on the map as the dominant soils of some of the larger river valleys of Mexico, Guatemala, Honduras, Nicaragua and Costa Rica. In these valleys Fluvisols are generally associated with Gleysols; they are often farmed together and the land-use pattern on the two soils may be similar. Not shown on the soil map are the many small areas of Fluvisols in the narrow valleys of Central America. Their total area is not large but they are of great importance to the farmers in the mountainous landscapes. In some countries the volume of production from these mountain valley Fluvisols represents a considerable proportion of the total subsistence crops available to the people.

The precise land-use pattern depends as much on local market requirements as on regional climatic factors; Fluvisols permit a wide range of utilization. For many crops Eutric Fluvisols are little modified by fertilizer applications; Dystric Fluvisols, on the other hand, respond to regular dressings of nitrogen and phosphate, and crops also benefit from added potash.

Suitability. Under either traditional or improved systems of management Fluvisols produce well. There is some danger to crops from sudden flooding in the smaller valleys, and occasionally crops suffer from more prolonged flooding in the larger valleys.

K. Kastanozems

Use. Kastanozems occur only in Mexico, around the periphery of the more desertic Xerosols and Yermosols. A large proportion of these soils occur on steep mountain slopes as lithic phases, and their main agricultural value is for extensive grazing. The deeper Kastanozems on less accentuated landscapes are used for grain crops, potatoes, agave, beans, cotton, and for pasturage. Tomatoes, peppers, onions, melons, and many other vegetables that appear in abundance in Mexico City markets, are produced chiefly on Kastanozems, as well as many fruit crops.

Suitability. At elevations below about 2 600 m traditional farmers grow maize and small fruits; at higher elevations they grow small plots of wheat and potatoes. Yields vary widely from year to year depending on the intensity and distribution of seasonal rainfall.

Under improved management systems (often with irrigation), the Kastanozems are very productive because they have a high natural fertility and moderately high organic matter content. Crop yields are improved by use of fertilizers, but the amounts required are usually not large. Under irrigation some care is needed to ensure that Kastanozems with an argillic B horizon (Luvic Kastanozems) or with a cemented subsoil horizon (duripan or petrocalcic phases) do not suffer from excess watering, leading to increased salt content on drying out. Lithic phases of these soils occurring on landscapes of gentle relief can be irrigated and used for improved pastures or fodder crops, but lithic phases on hilly or mountainous landscapes are usually left for seasonal grazing.

L. Luvisols

Lc. CHROMIC LUVISOLS

Use. These soils occur in many parts of Mexico and Central America and in some of the larger Caribbean islands, being most common in regions with a subhumid climate with a well-marked dry season. They occur over a wide range of altitude (from near sea level to over 2 000 m) and appear to be derived from a vast assortment of parent materials, ranging from limestones and other calcareous sedimentary rocks to strongly weathered volcanic tuffs and volcanic ash. A broad range of crops can be grown on these soils: in the cooler Mexican upland regions potatoes, wheat and other small grains, apricots and peaches, fibre and oil crops, and pasture; at the other end of the climatic range on the tropical Pacific foothills and lowlands of El Salvador, Nicaragua and Panama the main crops are sugarcane, coffee and rice, and pasture.

Suitability. Under traditional management, Chromic Luvisols are moderately good farming soils. Yields are seldom high, but they are fairly consistent year after year on the same area. Traditional farmers who have learnt the advantage of applying phosphate fertilizers to their small plots have been satisfied by the increased yields obtained, particularly with Chromic Luvisols derived from volcanic ash parent materials.

Under improved management systems both phosphate and nitrogen are essential for good yields of almost all crops, but fertilizing takes second place to irrigation, which is the most important step to satisfactory economic levels of production from these soils. In some areas lithic and petrocalcic phases are widespread, and in others the surface may be stony or bouldered. Any of these factors may limit the application of modern technology, restricting usage to pasturage, or necessitating an expensive programme of stone removal or contouring and terracing. On Chromic Luvisols generally, which are seldom flat, great care is needed to ensure that application of irrigation water does not result in serious erosion.

Lf. FERRIC LUVISOLS

Use. In Mexico these soils occur occasionally on the coastal lowlands, but they become more widespread in the interior ranges of Guatemala, Honduras and Nicaragua, usually as associate soils with Dystric Cambisols or with Acrisols. They are formed mainly from siliceous parent materials, under tropical humid environmental conditions. In the mountain ranges lithic phases are common. Cassava, maize, coffee and cocoa are grown on a family subsistence scale on these soils, which are also used for rough pasturage.

Suitability. For traditional farmers the natural fertility of Ferric Luvisols is just enough to permit fair yields of maize on land used at six- to ten-year intervals. Phosphate and nitrogen deficiency symptoms are evident in maize plants grown under this system.

Under improved farming systems crop yields are uneconomic except with regular fertilizer programmes. Nitrogen and phosphate are needed for all crops and for pasture; potash is required as well in banana and plantain plantations. Drainage problems occur during the rainy season.

Lg. GLEYIC LUVISOLS

Use. Gleyic Luvisols occur on flattish to undulating landscapes on the coastal lowlands of Mexico (Tabasco, Oaxaca) and British Honduras, and on some upland plateaus in British Honduras, Guatemala and Mexico as associate soils with Orthic Luvisols and Acrisols. They are used mainly for growing rice or rough pasturage.

Suitability. These soils combine low natural fertility with slow internal drainage and are difficult to handle with traditional methods. Small farmers on these soils chiefly depend for a living on rather poor crops of sugarcane and nonirrigated rice, root crops and a few cattle.

Improved technology can greatly better these soils, but the cost may be high because both the internal and external movement of water must be improved. Internal drainage conditions are so poor that any prolonged period of rain causes flooding. Since lateral movement of water in the soil is slow, open drains do little to ameliorate this condition, and trials with mole draining have not been uniformly successful. Reshaping the soil surface into long ridges and swales to speed up surface run-off greatly diminishes the risk of surface flooding but the broad drainage ways must remain permanently under pasture (or natural regrowth vegetation) to control erosion. Mechanized rice-growing is possible on these improved soils, but compaction resulting from the use of heavy harvesting machinery when the soils are wet may cause further deterioration of internal drainage. Long rotation between grass and rice crops seems to be the most logical answer.

Lp. PLINTHIC LUVISOLS

Use. Plinthic Luvisols occur mainly as associate soils with Ferric and Gleyic Luvisols and Plinthic Acrisols, on low Pleistocene terrace systems of the eastern coastal lowlands of Mexico (Tabasco), British Honduras, Guatemala, Honduras and Nicaragua. In British Honduras they occur in association with Plinthic Gleysols and Planosols. They are used chiefly for extensive grazing. Rice-growing experiments are in progress.

Suitability. Plinthic Luvisols have seriously impeded internal drainage and low natural fertility. Traditional farmers use them for natural pasturage only, and until recently had not applied improved technology on these soils. Trials with rice cultivation have shown that the drainage problems are similar to those on Gleyic Luvisols but rather more difficult to overcome. If rain should fall during harvesting operations, either the crop has to be abandoned or serious damage of the prepared soil surface must be accepted.

Lv. VERTIC LUVISOLS

Use. Vertic Luvisols are derived principally from volcanic mudflow conglomerates and tuffs, under subhumid and humid tropical conditions. They occur mainly in Mexico, at the inner margin of the coastal lowlands, and in Guatemala, El Salvador and Nicaragua at various elevations. They are used for sugarcane, cotton, rice, coffee, citrus, and pasture. Locally they occur as lithic and duric phases.

Suitability. For traditional farmers the moderately high natural fertility of these soils makes them attractive for growing food crops during the rainy months. During the dry months they are usually left fallow and used for pasturage.

Under improved management, irrigation is necessary for economic yields of sugarcane and cotton. Most crops respond to additions of phosphate and nitrogen.

N. Nitosols

Nd. DYSTRIC NITOSOLS

Use. Dystric Nitosols occur in Mexico, British Honduras, Honduras, Guatemala, Nicaragua, Costa Rica, El Salvador, Panama, Cuba, Haiti, the Dominican Republic and many of the smaller Caribbean islands. In some eroded areas they are represented by lithic phases. They are usually derived from basic intrusive rocks, basic lavas or basic volcanic tuffs, under humid and subhumid, tropical and subtropical climates. They are widely used for coffee, cocoa and citrus, and for pasture and subsistence crops (mainly maize and beans). On the humid tropical lowlands they are used for bananas, sugarcane and rice.

Suitability. For traditional farmers these Nitosols are valuable because they are usually fairly deep and well drained, and of just adequate fertility to yield crops that satisfy the needs of the small farmer. In the few localities where farmers have become accustomed to using phosphates as a regular part of their farming operations, much better yields can be obtained.

Under improved management, regular use of phosphatic fertilizer and normal precautions against erosion are the important factors. In some areas the lithic phases of these soils are being successfully managed under coffee plantations, or under pasture for beef cattle, but great care in management is needed to guard against accelerated erosion.

Ne. Eutric Nitosols

Use. Eutric Nitosols are of more limited distribution than Dystric Nitosols in Central America. They occur scarcely at all in British Honduras, Guatemala, Honduras and Nicaragua, and they are rare in the larger Caribbean islands, although some of the smaller islands, such as Grenada, are well endowed. They are generally deep soils with good drainage and high natural fertility, derived from basic parent materials (usually of volcanic origin) under subhumid, tropical and subtropical environments. They are used for maize, sugarcane, nutmeg, coffee, cocoa, beans, rice and pasture. Closely related soils derived from marine volcanic sediments and coral limestone occur in the Yucatán peninsula of Mexico, in Jamaica, Cuba, Haiti, the Dominican Republic, and several of the smaller Caribbean islands. This latter group of Eutric Nitosols is studded with outcrops of coral rock and normally has a high level of exchangeable calcium and a pH near neutral in the topsoil. Lithic phases are common, and the soils in general are rather excessively well drained. They are used in Yucatán for citrus, oilseed crops (sunflower, sesame), fibre crops (henequen), and for pasture.

Suitability. Under traditional management most small farmers achieve an adequate annual return from these soils, and if crop yields decline it is usually due to increasing erosion of topsoil material.

Erosion is also the main problem for farmers applying improved systems of management. On slopes steeper than 12 percent contour cultivation should be mandatory, and indeed is advisable on slopes as gentle as 5 percent. Phosphatic fertilizers should be used from time to time to sustain production.

O. Histosols

Use. Histosols have a very limited distribution in this map region: they occur in small areas as associates of Andosols on the higher elevations of the volcanic mountains, and as a narrow strip along the eastern coastline from British Honduras southward in association with Regosols and Gleysols. Along the coast they are mainly Dystric Histosols and are derived from the organic residues of mangrove forests mixed with coastal alluvium. Histosols also occur in Cuba. They are not widely used for agriculture.

Suitability. Histosols are of no interest to traditional farmers owing to their high and usually saline water table. Improved technology could be applied to these soils but in most situations is likely to be unrewarding because of the high costs of dike construction, draining, and maintaining pumping stations. Other techniques involve leaching out soluble salts and consolidating and balancing the plant nutrients with a carefully planned fertilizer programme. These operations must be carried out before the soils can be brought into permanent production.

P. Podzols

These have not been mapped as dominant soils and are not shown on the map. They are exceptional in the region and occur — generally as Leptic Podzols — in very few soil associations, usually in a steep topography, together with Lithosols on acid rocks. Their total extension in the region is very limited. These soils are usually shallow, stony or steep and are unsuitable for agriculture; they are better used under forest.

Q. Arenosols

These do not occur as dominant soils and are not shown on the map. They are present in only two associations, one in Cuba and one in British Honduras. They have a very coarse texture, a low organic matter content, are extremely poor in nutrients and excessively drained. They have a very low fertility and are generally not suitable for agriculture.

R. Regosols

The Regosols of the map region occur in four distinct situations: around the Caribbean shores, where wind and tide deposit plentiful supplies of coral sand (Eutric Regosols) or quartz sand (Dystric Regosols); around the Pacific shores where similar aeolian and tidal deposits are generally rich in volcanic sand and pumice (Eutric Regosols); in the volcanic highlands near active vents, where freshly deposited cinders, scoria and coarse volcanic sand have not yet had time to enter on more than the initial stages of soil weathering; in desertic areas where aeolian sands and silts (often slightly salty) are intermittently accumulating.

Use. Coastal Regosols, both Eutric and Dystric, are commonly used for coconut plantations and, in areas in the humid tropics close to urban markets, for vegetables, especially melon. The volcanic highland Regosols are not used for agriculture except for rough pasturage and some coffee planting at their lower margins. The desert Regosols are used under irrigation in some localities to produce small grains, tomatoes, potatoes and oilseeds.

Suitability. Coastal farmers using traditional methods usually prefer Regosols because they are almost the only soils in the area that have no drainage problems. The farmers subsist on root crops (such as cassava) and coconuts, and market their melons, groundnuts and tomatoes. They employ seasonal mulch to conserve soil moisture and prolong the cropping period into the dry season for a few weeks.

Improved management with irrigation and the use of appropriate fertilizers can bring these soils into full production. Maintaining full production, however, requires frequent checking to ensure that soluble salts are not building up in the rooting zone and that wind erosion is not causing excessive loss of surface soil.

S. Solonetz

Use. These have not been mapped as dominant soils and are not shown on the soil map. They occur as inclusions in a number of soil associations. They are generally located in depressed and poorly drained areas where they are in association with Gleysols and Histosols. Gleyic Solonetz are the most frequent type of Solonetz in the region. These soils are imperfectly or poorly drained and land use appears to be closely related to drainage conditions as well as to the intensity of alkalinity, and is generally restricted to range or natural pasture, the carrying capacity of which is low.

Suitability. Under traditional agricultural systems these soils are rather unsuitable for the cultivation of crops. The impermeability of the subsurface horizons impedes root development and causes an unfavourable soil moisture regime. These soils may support grassland of fair quality but are difficult to use for nonirrigated crops.

Improved agriculture on Solonetz depends essentially on the possibility of replacing sodium by calcium in the exchange complex. The improvement of Solonetz has been extensively dealt with in the literature.

T. Andosols

Andosols are a soil group of major significance in this map region, not so much because of their geographic extent (which is less than that of many other groups) but by virtue of their considerable reserves of soil fertility which have supported large numbers of traditional farmers for many centuries. The majority of these soils are free draining, easy

to work at all moisture conditions, and have sufficient natural fertility for moderate yields of maize and other traditional subsistence crops. Their main limitations are erodability and deficiency of phosphate in forms available to growing plants.

Th. HUMIC ANDOSOLS

Use. Humic Andosols occur in the more humid areas of the neovolcanic plateau of Mexico and in Guatemala, El Salvador, Honduras, Costa Rica and Panama, and also in Martinique and several of the other Caribbean islands. They are used mainly for coffee, citrus, bananas, plantains and pasture, and various subsistence crops including beans and maize.

Suitability. The clay fraction of these soils has a high proportion of amorphous colloidal material which sharply reduces availability of soil phosphate. Traditional farmers seldom get reasonable yields of maize from these soils owing to this serious deficiency of phosphate. It can be reduced by heavy applications of lime and superphosphate, but few traditional farmers on these soils can afford to use fertilizer regularly. Under traditional management, after centuries of cropping, these soils frequently end up as rough pasturage.

Improved methods can do a lot, but initial development costs are often high. Under natural conditions these soils seldom dry; if they do they become dangerously erodable. For this reason the first stages of development should be toward establishing permanent grassland with heavy liming and dressings of superphosphate. This has to be maintained for a number of years until both the soil pH and available phosphate content reach a satisfactory level. From this stage onward arable-pasture rotation can be carried out, or permanent orchards can be established.

Tm. MOLLIC ANDOSOLS

Use. Mollic Andosols occur in the Tuxtla area of the Gulf of Mexico, in Guatemala, El Salvador, Honduras, Nicaragua and several of the smaller Caribbean islands. They are moderately productive but potentially erodable — less acid and of higher base and available phosphate status than the Humic Andosols. They are used for subsistence crops, tree crops (mainly coffee) and pasture. In the island of St. Vincent they are the main source of the regional arrowroot crop.

Suitability. Traditional farming on these soils is most successful where the farmers understand the need to use phosphatic fertilizers. Also, nitrogen with some potash is beneficial for many crops such as bananas and plantains.

Under improved farm management the Mollic Andosols are less expensive and far easier to handle than the Humic Andosols. Liming is rarely needed, but heavy dressings of phosphatic fertilizer are essential. Nitrogen is required for most crops and potash for a few. Erosion control measures are of vital importance.

To. Ochric Andosols

Ochric Andosols are probably more widespread than shown on the map, but their total area is still relatively insignificant. Their land use and farming suitability fall somewhere between the Humic and Mollic Andosols. They are reported from Mexico and Guatemala and one or two of the smaller Caribbean islands.

Tv. Vitric Andosols

Use. Vitric Andosols cover a large area of the neovolcanic uplands of Mexico and are well represented in El Salvador and Nicaragua. Less extensive areas occur in Guatemala, Costa Rica and Panama. They are also present in Martinique, Dominica, St. Vincent and other Caribbean islands. Their climatic range is wide, from subhumid warm temperate to humid tropical. Many kinds of crops can be grown on them, including wheat, tobacco, bananas, coffee and maize.

Suitability. Traditional farmers are on the whole quite satisfied with these soils, and those who have become accustomed to applying phosphates to their crops can usually make a good living from their farms. Deterioration of farmland is nearly always due to erosion which may be far from obvious in the early stages.

Improved management also tends to neglect the significance and danger of soil erosion, but if early measures are taken to minimize this and small but regular dressings of phosphate and nitrogen are applied, satisfactory yields of most crops can be assured. Irrigation is another modern technique that can be used to advantage with these soils where the dry season is prolonged, but in view of their high erodability sprinkler systems are far more satisfactory. Properly fertilized and watered, Vitric Andosols are among the best banana-growing soils in the Caribbean area.

V. Vertisols

Vertisols are widely scattered throughout the map region over a range of environments, from semiarid to humid and from temperate to tropical. They are formed mainly from calcareous and volcanic rocks and derived alluvial and colluvial materials.

Vp. Pellic Vertisols

Use. Depending partly on climatic factors, land use on Pellic Vertisols varies from small grains, peas, beans, and vegetables generally to sunflower and other oilseeds, to cotton, sugarcane, maize, and rice, to permanent beef and dairy pastures.

Suitability. The predominant clay in these soils is montmorillonite, which swells strongly in the rainy season so that the soils are tight and sticky but shrinks and becomes very hard and fissured in the dry season. For arable farming it is essential to carry out cultivation during the relatively brief period when the moisture conditions in the soil are neither too wet nor too dry. The large cracks that develop in these soils during the dry season can be detrimental to tree roots; the low porosity of the subsoil during the wet season further discourages tree root development. In short, although they are soils of high fertility and seldom respond to fertilizers, their physical problems are such that rice and livestock production are emerging as the more popular forms of land use.

Under traditional management some of the physical disadvantages of the soil are less restrictive. The Amerindian with his planting stick can plant at will, while the man with the tractor can only wait for the surface soil to dry. Traditional harvesting can also proceed almost independently of soil moisture conditions. On a small farm, trees can be heavily mulched to reduce water loss and cracking during the dry months, and there is no expense for fertilizers. A small farmer with primitive equipment can make a good living on Pellic Vertisols, especially if he grows some rice and maintains a few head of cattle on natural pasture.

The farmer using improved methods, with a large area of Pellic Vertisols under cultivation, needs a lot of machinery to take advantage of the relatively short interval when the soils are in the right stage of moisture for working. The problem is worse with annual crops such as cotton, and only a little better with crops of longer duration such as sugarcane. Irrigation can overcome the drying and shrinking of the clay, but because of the slow infiltration rate of the moist soil carefully controlled sprinkler systems are preferable. Where rainfall is intense during the rainy season, some effort must be made to improve the slow natural drainage of these soils. Open drains are not often very effective, and mole drains through the subsoil tend to have a short life. Landscape moulding into long wide ridges separated by shallow swales, permanently grassed and draining toward a main collector drain, is proving one of the best techniques for disposing of surplus rainwater.

Most crops require little or no fertilizers. Potash has been used to advantage on sugarcane on Pellic Vertisols in British Honduras, and phosphatic fertilizers are reported to increase yields on Pellic Vertisols originating from volcanic materials in Nicaragua. Supplements of sulfur, iron, molybdenum and zinc appear to be needed for some crops on these soils. Pellic Vertisols are also highly susceptible to erosion, and strip cropping (with grass) is advisable on slopes above 5 percent.

Vc. CHROMIC VERTISOLS

Use. Similar to Pellic Vertisols.

Suitability. In many respects these soils resemble the Pellic Vertisols although they are less well known, being of much more limited extent in the map region. They occur over small areas in Mexico, Guatemala and El Salvador. Phosphate is said to be important for optimum yields.

W. Planosols

Planosols occur to a minor extent, mainly in Mexico in the state of Tabasco, in the Petén sector of Guatemala, on the Caribbean lowlands of British Honduras, on the Pacific lowlands of Honduras and El Salvador, and in Nicaragua, Costa Rica, Panama, the Dominican Republic and Cuba. They are chiefly developed on low terraces of the coastal lowland plains, generally derived from Pleistocene sediments, and formed under moisture regimes ranging from subhumid to humid and under tropical temperatures. Eutric, Dystric and Humic Planosols have been recognized.

Use. Many of the Planosols are used only for rough pasturage; a few have been tried for sugarcane and other crops but with little success. They are being used for rice-growing in several areas with much better results.

Suitability. The chief characteristic of these soils is a tight and almost impervious clay horizon in the upper part of the subsoil. Since the soils are developed on flat or flattish topography, they become flooded during heavy rain and remain partially flooded for a considerable time. When no rain falls they dry out down to (and including) the upper part of the clay pan. Most Planosols have the additional disadvantage of low to very low soil fertility. Few plants have roots that can penetrate the subsoil pan, and even in nature the range of plants that can with-

stand the seasonal moisture extremes that are inevitable in these soils appears to be quite restricted. Rice seems to be one of the few crops that can, with the aid of fertilizers, produce reasonable yields.

On flattish and gently sloping land, a ring drain to stop extra surface water moving into the cropping area is sometimes advisable. If excess surface rainwater can be stored nearby to provide water for irrigation in the dry season, more than one rice crop can be grown in a year, but in most countries such refinements are still in the experimental stage.

Under improved management the farmer on these soils thus has a number of problems to cope with. The farmer using traditional and simple water control systems often gets only a small return for his efforts, barely sufficient to pay for his outlay on seed and fertilizer, and after a few attempts the land is usually allowed to revert to rough pasturage.

X. Xerosols

Xerosols occur only in desert areas of Mexico, forming a belt between the Yermosols of the driest parts of the region and the peripheral zone of Kastanozems. Haplic, Calcic and Luvic Xerosols have been mapped. Lithic and petrocalcic phases are very common.

Use. Most areas of Xerosols are used for extensive grazing only, but in some places water has been made available for irrigation and small grains, vegetables and potatoes are grown.

Suitability. Xerosols are well supplied with plant nutrients but these are seldom available to plants until water is supplied. Irrigation has to be applied to Xerosols with considerable care because of the occasional presence of drainage-impeding layers in the subsoil: an argillic layer in the case of Luvic Xerosols, and lime-cemented layers in the petrocalcic phases. Where these occur at shallow depth parts of the area irrigated can flood easily, and if the soils are subsequently allowed to dry out soluble salts will tend to accumulate at the soil surface. If the supply of irrigation water is correctly regulated the fertility inherent in the Xerosols will begin to show in rising crop yields, but the addition of nitrogenous fertilizer and sometimes iron and zinc may be required for optimum yields. The skilful application of improved technology can thus make the Xerosols truly fertile.

Traditional methods of farming on these soils are restricted to grazing the sparse natural vegetation. Pre-Columbian settlements in the area concentrated their agricultural efforts on the associated Fluvisols and Regosols of the main river valleys.

Y. Yermosols

Yermosols occur only in Mexico, in the driest parts of the north and northwest, and are contiguous with much larger extensions of similar soils in North America.

Use. The primitive agriculturists in this area made some use of alluvial soils along the river valleys and colluvial fan soils in the vicinity of emergent spring water, but the main expanse of desert had no agricultural value for them apart from sparse grazing when ephemeral plants appeared after rain. With the advent of modern technology, irrigation began to make agriculture feasible on Yermosols although most schemes are directed more at the alluvial and colluvial soils, and Regosols associated with the older, true desert soils. Garden crops, cereals, fodder, oilseed and fibre crops and some fruits are grown on the irrigated soils.

Suitability. In places where irrigation has been extended on the older and more stable areas of the desert surface, the application of irrigation water requires considerable skill because of clay or cemented gravel horizons, often at no great depth beneath the surface. Cementation is partly due to salts that can dissolve in the irrigation water. With sufficient water these can be leached down to lower levels where they will interfere less with growing plants, otherwise the salts may move upward and interfere with fertilizers by making the rooting zone too saline or alkaline.

Vegetable legumes and leguminous fodder crops need phosphate as well as nitrogen. In addition to the soluble salts originally in the soil and those that are added in fertilizers, there is often a continual drift of fine salt crystals blown by the wind from the almost bare desert surrounding the irrigated area. The water used in irrigation also contains soluble salts. The improved technology required for farming Yermosols is quite sophisticated. The traditional farmer uses these soils only for extensive grazing after rain.

Z. Solonchaks

Solonchaks occur principally in Mexico in association with Yermosols. They are usually found near the lowest point in the desertic upland basins, sometimes developed in ancient lacustrine sediments. Small areas of Solonchaks occur within many existing irrigation projects and usually show up as trouble spots that should really be given special drainage-irrigation treatment to ensure that the soluble salts are kept to a minimum.

Conclusions

Mexico, Central America and the Caribbean islands together form a region in which soils of fair to good natural fertility easily outnumber soils of low natural fertility. Cambisols, Luvisols and Andosols are common. Most of the soils of lower fertility can be brought to a satisfactory level of production with relatively simple modern agricultural techniques. Areas of soils with deficiency of water (chiefly Yermosols, Xerosols, arid-zone Lithosols and Regosols), and soils with salinity problems (Solonchaks and Solonetz) are restricted mainly to the Mexican sector. Soils with drainage problems (some Gleysols, Fluvisols, Planosols and Vertisols) are of relatively minor extent in the region and their limitations are usually local. There are few areas of soils presenting problems for which special solutions need to be found.

Throughout the region the main technical limitations to improved farming systems stem from the steep nature of much of the landscape: Lithosols are quite common and many soils are present only in their lithic phase. On such soils modern techniques can have only limited application, and the chief source of agricultural production will continue to be the traditional family unit. Greater effort is needed to make the planting of permanent tree crops for specific soils and climatic conditions a profitable source of farm income, so that the area used for subsistence crops can be reduced.

The region's natural pattern of soil resources is thus suited to high and sustained agricultural production. The fact that it is not among the more prosperous farming areas of the world may be explained by comparing the pattern of land use, past and present, with the soil pattern. First, the present pattern of land use is basically the same as it was over a century ago. Traditional farming is entrenched; the main difference is that it is now much more intensified. Second, the steady rise in population has put excessive pressure on most of the better soils, to the point where maintaining local food production, even at subsistence level, leaves little to contribute to national urban requirements or to overseas markets. This is especially true of the highland soils (Andosols, Dystric and Eutric Cambisols, and Lithosols).

Within the region there are considerable areas of soils that are scarcely used or used to only a fraction of their true capacity. These are chiefly in the lowlands. With relatively minor adjustments in traditional methods these soils can become quite productive.

MORPHOLOGICAL, CHEMICAL AND PHYSICAL PROPERTIES OF MEXICAN AND CENTRAL AMERICAN SOILS: DATA FROM SELECTED PROFILES

In this appendix data are presented on typical profiles representing several of the major soil units that occur as dominant or associated soils on the Soil Map of Mexico and Central America.

The profiles were selected from published and unpublished material available to the project. Whenever possible acknowledgement is made to the sources of the data that have been used.

The purpose of including these descriptions and tables is to help define more clearly the nature of the soil units used in the map. Naturally, the description and analyses of one or two profiles will not show the range of characteristics within such broad units, but combined with the definitions in Volume I and with the descriptions and analyses in the other volumes they should at least help to establish the concepts on which the legend is based.

For most of the soil units only one profile is described, but for some of the more extensive units two profiles are presented to give some impression of the range that can be expected.

The data have been set out systematically to include most of the items generally available in survey reports. With such a variety of sources (data from five countries) there is considerable diversity in the information supplied. However, an attempt has been made to present it as uniformly as possible so that valid comparisons can be made. Where established standards such as the U.S. Department of Agriculture *Soil survey manual* (1951) have been used, there is no difficulty. In other places there may be some uncertainty in the definition of terms and care in interpretation is needed.

Analytical data were available for a few profiles only, located in Costa Rica and Mexico. The descriptions, analytical data and methods of the profiles in Costa Rica were taken from theses by M. Macías and C. Luzuriaga.[1]

---

[1] Luzuriaga T., C. *Propiedades Morfológicas, Físicas y Químicas y Clasificación de Seis Andosoles de Costa Rica.* Turrialba, Costa Rica, Instituto Interamericano de Ciencias Agrícolas de la Organización de los Estados Americanos. (Thesis) – Macías V., M. *Propiedades Morfológicas, Físicas, Químicas y Clasificación de Ocho Latosoles de Costa Rica.* Turrialba, Costa Rica, Instituto Interamericano de Ciencias Agrícolas de la Organización de los Estados Americanos. (Thesis)

Five descriptions and analytical data of profiles in Mexico were taken from the guide to the field tour of the Latin American Seminar on the Systematic Evaluation of Land and Water Resources, held in Mexico in November 1971.

Presentation of data

Whenever possible the data have been taken from the original documents without alteration. However, some changes have been made for the sake of brevity or uniformity of presentation.

SITE DESCRIPTION

The information used to describe the site is as follows:

Location: An attempt was made to locate the site of each profile by the distance and direction from a main town and by latitude and longitude. In many reports the information given was insufficient to determine siting accurately.

Altitude: The altitude is given in metres above mean sea level.

Physiography: Where possible, the nature of the landscape as well as the slope at the profile site are given.

Parent material: Sometimes parent rock is given under this heading.

Vegetation: Normally both information and space are insufficient to allow a description of the site vegetation, so only general terms are given (for example, grassland, deciduous forest).

Climate: Average annual rainfall and temperature are given when available.

PROFILE DESCRIPTION

The profile descriptions have been written in the pattern outlined in FAO, *Guidelines for soil profile description*. The information is given in the order: colour, mottling, texture, structure, consistency, other items. Horizon designations have been altered to conform with the definitions given in Volume I. Where they were not included in the original description, they have been added on the basis of the descriptive and analytical information available.

ANALYSES

pH is usually measured at a 1 : 1 soil/water ratio; a 1 : 2 ratio is used in Mexico.

Measurements in $1N$ KCl and $0.01N$ CaCl$_2$ were also made.

Cation exchange: ammonium acetate method at pH 7.

Organic matter: Walkley-Black method for C and Kjeldahl method for N.

Particle size analysis: A modified hydrometer method is used in Costa Rica.

Both the hydrometer and pipette methods were used in Mexico. The following particle size ranges are separated:

coarse sand   2 000 — 500 μ
fine sand   500 — 50 μ
silt   50 —   2 μ
clay   below   2 μ

Textures are found by use of the triangular texture diagram in the U.S. *Soil survey manual.*

Other analyses are explained in the tables where necessary.

LIST OF SOIL PROFILES

Symbol and unit			Country	Page
Ah	ACRISOL	Humic	Costa Rica	66
Ah		Humic	Costa Rica	68
Bc	CAMBISOL	Chromic	Mexico	72
Bv		Vertic	Mexico	70
E	RENDZINA		Mexico	73
Fp	FERRALSOL	Plinthic	Honduras	73
Hh	PHAEOZEM	Haplic	Mexico	74
Je	FLUVISOL	Eutric	Mexico	76
Kk	KASTANOZEM	Calcic	Mexico	78
Kk		Calcic	Mexico	80
Lc	LUVISOL	Chromic	Mexico	81
Lc		Chromic	El Salvador	82
Lg		Gleyic	Mexico	83
Nd	NITOSOL	Dystric	Nicaragua	84
Ne		Eutric	Mexico	85
Sg	SOLONETZ	Gleyic	Mexico	86
Tm	ANDOSOL	Mollic	El Salvador	92
Tv		Vitric	Costa Rica	88
Tv		Vitric	Costa Rica	90
Vp	VERTISOL	Pellic	Mexico	93
We	PLANOSOL	Eutric	Honduras	94
Xl	XEROSOL	Luvic	Mexico	95
Yl	YERMOSOL	Luvic	Mexico	96

HUMIC ACRISOL   Ah

Unnamed soil	Costa Rica
Macías, 1969	Profile CR55
Location	San Jorge de Arenal, 34 km NE of Quesada in Alajuela province, 10º34'N, 84º17'W
Altitude	300 m
Physiography	Undulating terraces of large river valley
Parent material	Floods and mudflows of Pleistocene age
Vegetation	Natural pasture following tropical rainforest
Climate	Humid tropical, MAR 3 400 mm, MAT 26ºC

Profile description [1]

Ah	0-15 cm	Dark brown (7.5YR 3/2 moist) or dark reddish grey (5YR 4/2 dry) clay; strong fine subangular blocky; sticky, plastic, friable; hard; no clayskins; abundant fine roots; boundary clear, smooth.
AB	15-35 cm	Dark reddish brown (5YR 3/4 moist) or reddish brown (5YR 4/4 dry) clay; moderate medium subangular blocky; sticky, plastic, friable; hard; no clayskins; many fine roots; boundary clear, smooth.
BA	35-60 cm	Yellowish red (5YR 4/6 moist or 5YR 5/6 dry) clay; moderate coarse subangular blocky; sticky, plastic, friable; hard; continuous coarse clayskins; common very fine roots; boundary gradual, smooth.
Bt1	60-90 cm	Yellowish red (5YR 5/6 moist) or reddish brown (5YR 5/4 dry) clay; moderate coarse subangular blocky; sticky, plastic, friable; hard; continuous coarse clayskins; few very fine roots; boundary gradual, smooth.
Bt2	90-140 cm	Reddish brown (5YR 4/4 moist or 5YR 5/4 dry) clay; few distinct clear medium mottles; moderate coarse subangular blocky; sticky, plastic, friable; hard; continuous coarse clayskins; very few fine roots; boundary gradual, smooth.
BC	140-190 cm	Reddish brown (5YR 4/6 moist and 5YR 5/4 dry) clay; few distinct clear medium mottles; moderate coarse subangular blocky; sticky, plastic, friable; hard; moderate continuous coarse clayskins; very few fine roots.

---

[1] See Volume I for definition of horizons.

Horizon	Depth cm	pH		Cation exchange me %									CaCo₃ %
		H₂O	CaCl₂	CEC	TEB	% BS	Ca	Mg	K	Na	Al	H	
Ah	0—15	5.3	4.8	25.4		21	3.9	1.3	0.12		3.2		
AB	—35	5.6	4.9	24.2		16	2.8	0.9	0.06		2.2		
BA	—60	5.7	5.0	28.3		13	2.6	1.1	0.05		1.8		
Bt1	—90	5.5	4.5	28.4		9	1.8	0.8	0.03		2.8		
Bt2	—140	5.6	4.6	27.0		5	0.8	0.6	0.03		4.1		
BC	—190	5.1	4.4	26.7		4	0.7	0.4	0.03		6.0		

Horizon	Soluble salts	Organic matter				Particle size analysis %						Flocc. index
		% C	% N	C/N	% OM	Stones	Coarse sand	Fine sand	Silt	Clay	Texture	
Ah		5.5	0.50	11	9.4		1.0	12	10	77	clay	
AB		1.9	0.18	11	3.4		0.2	3	14	84	clay	
BA		1.5	0.14	10	2.5		0.2	3	5	92	clay	
Bt1		1.0	0.10	10	1.6		1.0	2	6	92	clay	
Bt2		0.8	0.08	10	1.3		0.6	4	4	92	clay	
BC		0.5	0.07	7	0.8		1.2	5	2	91	clay	

Horizon	SiO₂	Al₂O₃	Fe₂O₃	TiO₂	MnO	P₂O₅	SiO₂/Al₂O₃	SiO₂/R₂O₃	Al₂O₃/Fe₂O₃
Ah	40.0	21.2	13.5						
AB	39.2	23.4	14.0						
BA	38.6	21.2	13.3						
Bt1	37.7	29.3	13.0						
Bt2	37.7	26.2	13.3						
BC	37.3	20.4	13.3						

6

HUMIC ACRISOL Ah

Unnamed soil	Costa Rica
Macías, 1969	Profile CR46
Location	15 km S of town of Buenos Aires (Valley San Isidro del General) toward Panama, near Pan-American Highway, in province of Puntarenas, approximately 9º03'N, 83º17'W
Altitude	400 m
Physiography	Old Pleistocene terraces, with undulating surfaces
Parent material	Pleistocene alluvium and sedimentary rocks
Vegetation	Natural pasture following semideciduous forest
Climate	Moist subhumid, tropical, 4-5 months dry season, MAR 2 700 mm, MAT 24.2ºC

Profile description

Ah	0-10 cm	Dark brown (10YR 3/3 moist, 10YR 4/3 dry) clay; moderate fine subangular blocky; slightly sticky, slightly plastic, friable; hard; no clayskins; frequent fine roots; slightly stony, 15 percent stones on surface; boundary clear, smooth.
AB	10-28 cm	Dark brown (7.5YR 4/4 moist) or brown (7.5YR 5/4 dry) clay; moderate medium subangular blocky; slightly sticky, slightly plastic; firm; hard; patchy thin clayskins; common fine roots; boundary clear, smooth.
BA	28-50 cm	Reddish brown (5YR 4/4 moist) or yellowish red (5YR 5/6 dry) clay; moderate medium subangular blocky; sticky, plastic; firm; hard; continuous thin clayskins; few fine roots; boundary clear, wavy.
Bt1	50-75 cm	Yellowish red (5YR 4/6 moist) or reddish yellow (5YR 6/6 dry) clay; mottled yellow-brown (10YR 5/6 moist); mottles common, fine, distinct; moderate medium subangular blocky; sticky, plastic; firm; hard; continuous thin clayskins; very few very fine roots; very fine subangular blocky microstructure; boundary gradual.
Bt2	75-100 cm	Yellowish brown (10YR 5/4 moist) or reddish yellow (5YR 7/6 dry) clay; mottled yellowish red (5YR 4/6 moist); mottles abundant, medium, distinct; moderate medium subangular blocky; sticky, plastic; firm; hard; thin discontinuous clayskins; no roots; red and yellow iron concretions; boundary diffuse, wavy.
BC	100-150 cm	Yellow brown (10YR 5/6 moist) or reddish yellow (7.5YR 7/6 dry) clay; mottled pale grey (10YR 6/4 moist); mottles common, coarse, distinct; moderate medium subangular blocky; sticky, plastic; firm; hard; very thin continuous clayskins; no roots.

Horizon	Depth cm	pH		Cation exchange me %										CaCO₃ %
		H₂O	CaCl₂	CEC	TEB	% BS	Ca	Mg	K	Na	Al	H	
Ah	0—10	4.9	4.2	24.0		4	0.5	0.1	0.2		16.5		
AB	—28	5.2	4.3	19.8		2	0.2	0.02	0.1		16.0		
BA	—50	5.5	4.3	21.1		1	0.1	0.04	0.1		13.1		
Bt1	—75	5.6	4.4	21.4		1	0.1	0.04	0.1		13.0		
Bt2	—100	5.7	4.4	22.6		1	0.1	0.04	0.04		13.6		
BC	—150	5.8	4.4	23.8		1	0.1	0.04	0.03		12.9		

Horizon	Soluble salts		Organic matter				Particle size analysis %						Flocc. index
			% C	% N	C/N	% OM	Stones	Coarse sand	Fine sand	Silt	Clay	Texture	
Ah			5.3	0.30	18	9		6	15	9	70	clay	
AB			2.5	0.15	17	4		1	7	11	81	clay	
BA			1.2	0.08	15	2		3	5	14	78	clay	
Bt1			0.8	0.06	14	1		2	6	19	73	clay	
Bt2			0.8	0.05	17	1		3	7	21	69	clay	
BC			0.3	0.04	7	0.6		1	10	21	68	clay	

Horizon	SiO₂	Al₂O₃	Fe₂O₃	TiO₂	MnO	P₂O₅	$\frac{SiO_2}{Al_2O_3}$	$\frac{SiO_2}{R_2O_3}$	$\frac{Al_2O_3}{Fe_2O_3}$
Ah	35.9	27.1	11.8				2.3	1.8	3.6
AB	37.4	28.5	12.1				2.2	1.8	3.7
BA	37.4	28.0	12.1				2.3	1.8	3.6
Bt1	37.4	28.1	12.2				2.3	1.8	3.6
Bt2	39.1	27.6	12.1				2.4	1.9	3.6
BC	36.2	27.7	12.1				2.2	1.7	3.6

VERTIC CAMBISOL	Bv
Unnamed soil	Mexico
Garza and Camacho, 1971	
Location	23 km from Atotonilco el Alto on highway to Guadalajara, 20º32'N, 102º43'W
Altitude	About 1 500 m
Physiography	Floodplain
Parent material	Fine textured alluvium from basalts
Vegetation	Cultivated, chickpea and wheat
Climate	Dry winter, MAR 820 mm; average maximum temperature 31ºC, minimum 6.5ºC

Profile description

Ap	0-25 cm	Reddish brown (5YR 4/4 dry), dark reddish brown (2.5YR 3/3 moist) clay with black mottling; extremely hard dry, friable moist; slightly plastic and slightly sticky wet; frequent fine tubular pores; very few fine roots; clear boundary.
Bw	25-60 cm	Reddish brown (5YR 4/4 dry) and dark reddish brown (5YR 3/3 moist) clay; fine weak subangular blocky; few black mottles; hard dry, friable moist; plastic and slightly sticky wet; many very fine tubular pores; few very fine roots; clear boundary.
C1	60-94 cm	Dark reddish brown (5YR 3/3 moist) clay; fine weak angular blocky; few black mottles; hard dry, friable moist; slightly plastic and sticky wet; many very fine pores; very few fine roots; clear boundary.
C2	94-130 cm	Dark reddish brown (5YR 2/3 moist) clay; fine weak subangular blocky; frequent black mottles; very hard dry, friable moist; slightly plastic and sticky wet; many fine tubular pores, very few fine roots.

Horizon	Depth cm	pH		Cation exchange me %									CaCO₃ %
		H₂O	KCl	CEC	TEB	% BS	Ca	Mg	K	Na	Al	H	
Ap	0—25	6.2		22.20		45				1.38			
Bw	—60	5.8		21.70		42				0.10			
C1	—94	5.7		28.10		35				0.15			
C2	—130	6.3		21.10		57				0.24			

Horizon	Soluble salts		Organic matter				Particle size analysis %						Flocc. index
			% C	% N	C/N	% OM	Stones	Coarse sand	Fine sand	Silt	Clay	Texture	
Ap			1.43	0.012	11.9	2.48		26.86		26	47.14	clay	
Bw			1.19	0.23	5.17	2.06		22.86		24	53.14	clay	
C1			0.70	0.09	7.78	1.22		22.86		34	43.14	clay	
C2			0.79	0.09	8.75	1.36		26.86		28	45.14	clay	

CHROMIC CAMBISOL   Bc

Umán clay	Mexico
Wright, 1967	
Location	3 km S of town of Umán on road to Uxmal, roadside borrow pit
Altitude	About 45 m
Physiography	Flattish and gently rolling uplifted coral reef; numerous limestone outcrops and soils mainly in shallow pockets in the old reef surface
Parent material	Probably mainly marine coastal mud, etc., with some volcanic ash drifted on to reef and uplifted in situ
Vegetation	Low deciduous forest, mainly leguminous species
Climate	Dry subhumid, tropical, MAR about 800 mm, MAT about 25°C

Profile description

Ah   **0-15 cm**   Dark reddish brown (2.5YR 3/4 dry, 7.5YR 2/4 moist) clay; friable when moist, loose when dry; moderately sticky and very strongly plastic when wet; very strong (cast) granular structure, breaking to very fine granules and crumbs; no clayskins; many roots; boundary indistinct.

Bw   **15-27 cm**   Dark reddish brown (2.5YR 3/6 dry, 2.5YR 3/4 moist) clay; almost massive structure in place and very porous, breaking easily in hand to moderately developed coarse subangular blocky structure, and breaking further to weakly developed fine and very fine angular blocks, coarse and fine granules and crumbs; no clayskins; consistency slightly firm when moist, slightly hard when dry; slightly sticky and very strongly plastic when wet; slightly compact and fairly hard to dig at all moisture contents; roots common; boundary abrupt; very hard white limestone with a " washed " surface.

(No analyses available)

NOTE : Profile described is slightly deeper than average since it is located near a slight depression in the landscape and there is a large fissure in the underlying limestone at 1-2 metres from the site described; the fissure is filled with only lightly compacted clay and serves as a channel for drainage of the depression.

RENDZINA E

Polyuc series **Wright, 1967**	Mexico
Location	Chunhuhub irrigation settlement area, Yucatán
Altitude	About 1 m
Physiography	Summit of low rolling ridge in generally rolling and undulating coral limestone plain
Parent material	Mainly coral limestone
Vegetation	Under cultivation, after semideciduous forest
Climate	Dry to moist subhumid, tropical, strong dry season of 3-5 months, MAR about 1 200 mm, MAT about 25°C

Profile description

A   0-18 cm   Brownish black gravelly (7.5YR 3/1 dry, 7.5YR 3/1 moist) clay; friable moist, rather soft dry but with slightly hardened peds; slightly sticky and very plastic wet; strongly developed fine angular blocky structure with some coarse granules; roots abundant; boundary highly irregular but quite sharp.

C   18+   Strongly fragmented limestone and limestone gravel, with stained surface (dull orange to orange 5YR 6/4-6/6); some limestone fragments show pinkish colour when broken; soil continues on down fissures in limestone and has more brownlish colour than topsoil.

(No analyses available)

PLINTHIC FERRALSOL Fp

Silmacia series **Simmons, 1968**	Honduras
Location	Mosquitia region, along Ras-Ras Leimus road, 4 km E of junction with road to Suji
Altitude	Lower than 150 m
Physiography	Gently undulating, almost flat marine terrace
Parent material	Clayey alluvial deposit
Vegetation	Clear pine forest with dense grass cover

Profile description

Ah   0-10 cm   Brown to dark brown (7.5YR 4/4 moist) silt loam to silty clay loam; very fine weak granular structure; friable, slightly sticky and plastic; pH 5.5.

AB   10-20 cm   Strong brown (7.5YR 5/6 moist) silt loam to silty clay loam; fine weak granular structure; friable, slightly sticky and plastic; pH 5.0.

Bs   20-60 cm   Red (2.5YR 5/8 moist) clay; fine weak subangular blocky structure; friable, slightly sticky and plastic; common sesquioxide concretions, especially in lower part; pH 5.0.

BC   60+   Reddish yellow (5YR 6/8 moist) clay with yellowish red (5YR 4/8) reticular mottling and few sesquioxide concretions in upper part; pH 4.5.

(No analyses available)

HAPLIC PHAEOZEM   Hh

Tepatepec series   Mexico
Rodríguez and Jiménez, 1971

Location	Near town of Tepatepec, Hidalgo state, 20°16'N, 99°12'W
Altitude	2 020 m
Physiography	Valley, bottomland, very gentle slope
Parent material	Weathering material from rhyolitic tuffs
Vegetation	Cultivated, wheat
Climate	Mild semiarid with dry not well-defined winter

Profile description

Ap   0-25 cm   Dark yellowish brown (2.5Y 4/1 dry), very dark brown (7.5YR 2/2 moist) clay; coarse subangular blocky; very hard dry, friable moist; plastic and sticky wet; no HCl reaction; common fine and very fine roots; clear boundary.

AB   25-35 cm   Dark yellowish brown (2.5Y 4/1 dry), dark brown (7.5YR 3/2 moist) clay loam to clay; coarse subangular blocky; slightly hard dry, friable moist; plastic and sticky wet; no HCl reaction; few fine and very fine roots; gradual boundary.

Bw1   35-55 cm   Very dark brown (7.5YR 4/1 dry) and (7.5YR 2/2 moist) clay; medium angular blocky; friable moist; plastic and sticky wet; slight HCl reaction; few fine and coarse roots; clear boundary.

Bw2   55-85 cm   Dark brown (7.5YR 3/2 dry) and very dark brown (7.5YR 2/1 moist) clay loam or clay; medium angular blocky; hard dry, friable moist; plastic and sticky wet; no HCl reaction; very few roots; abrupt boundary.

C   85+   Pink (7.5YR 7/4 dry) and dark brown (7.5YR 3/4 moist); no HCl reaction.

Horizon	Depth cm	pH		Cation exchange me %										CaCO₃ %
		H₂O	KCl	CEC	TEB	% BS	Ca	Mg	K	Na	Al	H	
Ap	0—25	8.3	7.0	46.87						3.82			
AB	—35	8.4	7.0	38.75						4.51			
Bw1	—55	8.3	7.0	36.62						4.92			
Bw2	—85	8.3	6.3	36.24									
C	—85+												

Horizon	Soluble salts		Organic matter				Particle size analysis %						Flocc. index
			% C	% N	C/N	% OM	Stones	Coarse sand	Fine sand	Silt	Clay	Texture	
Ap			1.40	0.15					24.86	26.64	48.50	clay	
AB			1.20	0.09					27.86	29.64	42.50	clay	
Bw1			1.08	0.07					27.86	26.64	45.50	clay	
Bw2			0.94	0.05					28.86	28.64	42.50	clay	
C													

EUTRIC FLUVISOL   **Je**

Unnamed soil	Mexico
Rodríguez and Jiménez, 1971	
Location	SW of Salado river at Tlahuelilpa de Ocampo, Hidalgo state, 20º08'N, 99º15'W
Altitude	2 020 m
Physiography	Valley
Parent material	Recent alluvium from rhyolitic tuff, andesite and basalt
Vegetation	Cultivated, alfalfa
Climate	Temperate semidry with dry not well-defined winter

Profile description

Ap   **0-25 cm**
Dark greyish brown (10YR 4/2 dry), very dark brown (10YR 2/2 moist) clay or silty clay loam; coarse subangular blocky; very hard dry, friable moist; very plastic and sticky wet; slight HCl reaction; frequent fine roots; clear boundary.

Cl   **25-50 cm**
Greyish brown (10YR 5/2 dry), very dark greyish brown (10YR 3/2 moist) clay or silty clay loam; coarse and medium subangular blocky; hard dry, friable moist; very plastic and sticky wet; slight HCl reaction; few fine to very fine roots; clear boundary.

C2   **50-70 cm**
Greyish brown (10YR 5/2 dry), very dark brown (7.5YR 2/3 moist) silty clay loam or silty clay; coarse subangular blocky; very friable moist; plastic and sticky wet; slight HCl reaction; very few fine roots; abrupt boundary.

C3   **70-90 cm**
Very dark greyish brown (10YR 3/2 moist) silty clay loam or silty clay; structureless; friable moist; plastic and very sticky wet; slight HCl reaction; very few fine roots; abrupt boundary.

C4   **90-110 cm**
Dark brown (10YR 3/3 moist) silt loam; structureless; very friable moist; plastic and sticky wet; slight HCl reaction; few very fine roots; abrupt boundary.

C5   **110-160 cm**
Very dark grey to dark brown (7.5YR 3/1 moist) clay loam; structureless; friable moist; plastic and slightly sticky wet; very slight HCl reaction; few very fine roots; clear boundary.

C6   **160-200 cm**
Black to very dark brown (7.5YR 2/1 moist) clay loam to clay; structureless; friable moist; plastic and sticky wet; very slight HCl reaction; no roots.

Horizon	Depth cm	pH		Cation exchange me %										CaCO₃ %
		H₂O	KCl	CEC	TEB	% BS	Ca	Mg	K	Na	Al	H	
Ap	0—25	8.0	7.0	36.25						4.15			
C1	—50	8.3	7.0	33.75						4.09			
C2	—70	8.2	7.0	31.87						4.34			
C3	—90	8.3	7.0	33.75						3.94			
C4	—110	8.3	7.0	30.92						3.82			
C5	—160	8.3	6.9	45.92						3.21			
C6	—200	8.2	6.9	48.12						3.05			

Horizon	Soluble salts		Organic matter				Particle size analysis %						Flocc. index
			% C	% N	C/N	% OM	Stones	Coarse sand	Fine sand	Silt	Clay	Texture	
Ap			1.3	0.16					34.86	26.64	38.50	clay loam	
C1			0.20	0.05					33.86	30.64	35.50	clay loam	
C2			0.26	0.04					32.86	34.64	32.50	clay loam	
C3			0.06	0.03					30.86	36.64	32.50	clay loam	
C4			0.07	0.03					42.86	32.64	24.50	loam	
C5			0.46	0.05					24.86	41.64	33.50	clay loam	
C6			1.04	0.05					36.86	23.64	39.50	clay loam	

CALCIC KASTANOZEM   Kk

Progreso series	Mexico
Rodríguez and Jiménez, 1971	
Location	Meteorological station, Progreso, Hidalgo state
Altitude	About 2 000 m
Physiography	Valley, very gentle slope
Parent material	Rhyolitic tuff
Vegetation	Cultivated (recent deep ploughing)
Climate	Mild semiarid with dry not very defined winter

Profile description

Ap1   0-20 cm   Very dark grey (10YR 3/1 dry), very dark brown (10YR 2/2 moist) clay loam to loam; medium and coarse subangular blocky; slightly hard dry, friable moist; plastic and slightly sticky wet; slight HCl reaction; common fine to medium roots; clear boundary.

Ap2   20-40 cm   Very dark grey (10YR 3/1 dry), very dark brown (10YR 2/2 moist) clay loam; coarse angular blocky; very firm dry, firm moist; plastic and sticky wet; slight HCl reaction; common medium-sized roots; abrupt boundary.

AB   40-55 cm   Very dark brown (7.5YR 2/1 dry), black (7.5YR 1.7/1 moist) silt loam; medium subangular blocky; slightly hard dry, very friable moist; plastic and sticky wet; strong HCl reaction; few fine roots; abrupt boundary.

Ckm1   55-105 cm   Rhyolitic tuff cemented with calcium carbonate and in process of weathering.

Ckm2   105+   Rhyolitic tuff cemented with calcium carbonate.

Horizon	Depth cm	pH		Cation exchange me %									CaCO₃ %
		H₂O	KCl	CEC	TEB	% BS	Ca	Mg	K	Na	Al	H	
Ap1	0—20	7.7	7.0	35.62						1.97			
Ap2	—40	7.8	7.1	34.82						3.95			
AB	—55	8.0	7.0	46.87						2.05			

Horizon	Soluble salts		Organic matter				Particle size analysis %						Flocc. index
			% C	% N	C/N	% OM	Stones	Coarse sand	Fine sand	Silt	Clay	Texture	
Ap1			1.80	0.16				27.50		43.64	28.86	clay loam	
Ap2			1.68	0.05				47.86		24.64	27.50	clay loam	
AB			1.30	0.10				50.50		22.64	26.86	silt loam	

CALCIC KASTANOZEM   Kk

Unnamed soil		Mexico
Gile and Hawley, 1968		
Location		SE edge of San Isidro village, near Sacramento, Chihuahua state, about 35 km NW of Victoria hotel, Chihuahua city, and 400 m SE of Highway 45
Altitude		About 1 750 m
Physiography		High level fan or terrace surface between two major channels of the Arroyo Sacramento system
Parent material		Mainly rhyolitic, very gravelly sediments
Vegetation		Perennial grasses and scattered mesquite
Climate		MAR about 350 mm

Profile description

Ah   0-15   cm   Dark reddish grey (5YR 4/2 dry) or dark reddish brown (5YR 3/2 moist) very gravelly heavy sandy loam; very friable; fine roots common; noncalcareous; clear smooth boundary.

Bt   43-86   cm   Reddish brown (5YR 5/4 dry, 5YR 4/4 moist) very gravelly sandy clay loam; firm; few roots; sand grains and pebbles are clay-coated; some parts have six chroma and slightly redder; noncalcareous; abrupt wavy boundary.

Ck1   86-132   cm   White (7.5YR 9/2 dry) or pink (7.5YR 7/4 moist) carbonate-impregnated material discontinuously cemented; massive; slightly hard to very hard; no roots; few volumes of darker and redder Bt-like material; pebbles separated by carbonate; effervesces strongly; clear wavy boundary.

Ck2   132-234   cm   Dominantly pink (7.5YR 9/4-8/4 dry) and pink and light brown (7.5YR 7/4-6/4 moist) carbonate-impregnated material with common zones of Bt-like material (5YR-7.5YR 5/4 dry, 5YR-7.5YR 4/4 moist); massive; friable to very firm with some parts strongly cemented; no roots; effervesces strongly.

(No analyses available)

CHROMIC LUVISOL Lc

Chichén clay	Mexico
Wright and Taylor, 1967	
Location	Chichén Itzá, Yucatán
Altitude	About 70 m
Physiography	Small flat depression in rolling and broken limestone plain
Parent material	Probably volcanic tuff impurities in limestone and volcanic marine mud in place on coral when platform uplifted
Vegetation	Pasture after deciduous low forest
Climate	Dry to moist subhumid tropical, MAR about 800-1 000 mm, MAT 25°C

Profile description

Ah   0-8 cm   Dark brown (10YR 3/2-7.5YR 3/2 dry), reddish brown (5YR 4/4 crushed dry) clay; firm moist, slightly hard dry; slightly sticky and very plastic wet; moderately developed medium and coarse subangular blocky structure, breaking to very fine subangular and angular blocks and coarse (cast) granules; abundant roots; boundary gradual.

AB   8-18 cm   Dark reddish brown (2.5YR 3/4 dry and dry crushed) clay; firm moist, slightly hard dry; slightly to moderately sticky and moderately to strongly plastic wet; almost massive structure in place, breaking abruptly under pressure to weakly developed composite structure of very fine (cast) granules and fine to very fine subangular blocks; roots common; boundary indistinct.

Bt   18-60 cm   Reddish brown and red (5YR 3/4 and 2.5YR 3/4 dry, 2.5YR 3/6 rubbed dry, 5YR 3/4 moist) clay; patches firm and firm to friable moist, very slightly hard dry; slightly sticky and moderately to strongly plastic wet; more or less massive in place but shows very weakly developed coarse angular and subangular blocky structure on drying out, and these blocks break suddenly under light pressure to very fine rounded granules and powder; few roots; boundary irregular but abrupt.

R   60+   Very hard crystalline limestone of pinkish white colour; some large blocks, some smaller fragments, soil continuing down the fissures.

(No analyses available)

CHROMIC LUVISOL   Lc

Ozatlan series	El Salvador
Bourne, 1963	
Location	4 km E of Puente de Oro on littoral road, Usulután
Altitude	45 m
Parent material	Old volcanic ash

Profile description

Ah1   0-18 cm   Dark brown (7.5YR 3/2 dry) and very dark brown (7.5YR 2/2 moist) clay loam; moderate fine crumb; no clayskins; friable, slightly sticky, slightly plastic.

Ah2   18-35 cm   Brown (7.5YR 4/2 dry) and dark reddish brown (5YR 2/2 moist) clay loam; moderate fine crumb; no clayskins; friable, slightly sticky, slightly plastic.

Bt1   35-70 cm   Light reddish brown (5YR 6/3 dry) and dark reddish brown (5YR 3/2 moist) clay; primary structure, strong coarse angular blocky; secondary structure, moderate medium angular blocky; continuous faint clayskins on aggregates and in pores; firm; sticky and plastic; blocks have few black mottles on their surfaces.

Bt2   70-95 cm   Brown (7.5YR 4/3 dry) and dark brown (7.5YR 3/3 moist) silty clay; structure as above; clayskins and consistence as above.

BC1   95-145 cm   Dark greyish brown (10YR 4/3 dry) and dark brown (7.5YR 3/2 moist) clay loam; primary structure, moderate coarse angular blocky; secondary structure, moderate medium angular blocky; a few faint clayskins on aggregates and in pores; firm; sticky and plastic.

BC2   145-165 cm   Light grey (10YR 7/2 dry) and pale brownish grey (10YR 6/2 moist) with many medium prominent brown mottles (7.5YR 4/4) clay loam; moderate medium angular blocky; faint clayskins on peds, aggregates and in pores; firm; sticky and plastic.

C1   165-200 cm   Light grey (10YR 7/2 dry) and pale brown (10YR 6/3 moist) silt loam; weak medium angular blocky; no clayskins; firm; sticky and plastic.

C2   200-250 cm   Yellowish brown (10YR 5/4 dry) and dark brown to brown (7.5YR 4/3 moist) sandy clay loam; massive without clayskins; extremely firm.

(No analyses available)

GLEYIC LUVISOL   Lg

Chunhuhab clay   Mexico

Wright and Ruben Lopez, 1968

Location	Tampak irrigation development scheme, Quintana Roo Territory
Physiography	Flattish clay-filled depression in an undulating landscape of coral limestone
Parent material	Probably mainly colluvial material washed from surrounding slopes
Vegetation	Semideciduous forest with many swamp species
Climate	Moist subhumid, tropical with strong dry season of 5-6 months, MAR about 1 200 mm, MAT about 25°C

Profile description

Ah — 0-10 cm
Brownish black (10YR 2/2 moist) clay, firm moist, hard dry; very strongly sticky and plastic wet; moderately developed coarse and medium angular blocky structure, breaking to finer angular blocks and coarse granules; finely fissured when dry; no reaction to HCl; roots common; boundary distinct to sharp.

AB — 10-20 cm
Greyish yellow-brown (10YR 4/2 moist) clay with faint orange mottling and a few fine hard rounded manganese/iron nodules; very firm moist, very hard dry; very strongly sticky and plastic wet; strongly developed coarse to medium angular blocky structure, breaking to finer angular blocks; very few weak pressure faces, but soil cracks on drying out; no reaction to HCl; boundary distinct.

Btg1 — 20-30 cm
Dull yellowish orange (10YR 6/3 moist) coarsely and rather indistinctly mottled yellowish brown (10YR 5/3 moist) clay, with numerous, slightly hard, rounded or irregular manganese nodules; firm moist, hard dry; very strongly sticky and plastic wet; structure as for last horizon; very few and weak clayskins and pressure faces but shows cracks on drying out; no reaction to HCl; occasional to few roots; boundary gradual.

Btg2 — 30-75 cm
Yellowish brown (10YR 5/4 moist) clay with clear medium and large blotches of yellower colour (10YR 5/6 moist) and with numerous medium and fine, hard rounded, often shiny, iron/manganese nodules; very firm moist, very hard dry; very strongly sticky and plastic wet; very coarse angular (almost prismatic) blocky structure, breaks to finer blocks; clayskins abundant, and some pressure faces present, but no slickensides; no reaction to HCl; few roots; boundary merging.

Cg — 75-145 cm
Strong yellow brown (10YR 6/6 moist) clay, without mottles or blotches, and with only soft brown streaks of manganese accumulation; firm moist, very hard dry; very strongly sticky and plastic wet, irregular very coarse blocks breaking from an almost massive condition in place; numerous fragments of limestone present and some general reaction to HCl; very few roots; boundary abrupt.

R — 145+
Very hard white limestone with a smooth "washed" upper surface.

(No analyses available)

7

DYSTRIC NITOSOL   Nd

Unnamed soil	Nicaragua
Smyth, 1963	
Location	Road cut near Muhan river, at Muhan village, 210 km E of Managua
Altitude	About 500 m
Physiography	Crest of hill in rolling topography
Parent material	Basic volcanic tuff or basalt
Vegetation	Rough pasture after semideciduous forest

Profile description

Ah   0-15 cm   Reddish brown (5YR 4/3 dry) and dark reddish brown (5YR 3/3 moist) clay loam; fine angular blocky; friable, slightly plastic, slightly sticky; gradual; pH 5.7.

Bt1   15-60 cm   Dark reddish brown (5YR 3/3 dry and moist) clay; strong coarse angular blocky breaking easily to medium and fine angular blocky; plastic, slightly sticky; pH 4.8.

Bt2   60-120 cm   Distinctly mottled dark red (2.5YR 3/6 dry) and reddish brown (5YR 4/3 moist) clay; strong coarse angular blocky breaking easily to medium angular blocky; plastic, slightly sticky; strong clayskins on ped faces.

BC   120-200 cm   Prominently mottled (reticulate) dark red (2.5YR 3/6 dry) and reddish grey (5YR 5/2 moist) clay; strong clayskins on coarse angular blocky structure; pH 4.2.

(No analyses available)

EUTRIC NITOSOL	**Ne**	
Uxmal clay	Mexico	
Wright and McCracken, 1968		
Location	1 km SE of Uxmal hotel, in borrow pit used by cement industry, in Mérida, Yucatán	
Altitude	About 80 m	
Physiography	Broad shallow basin of Eocene coral limestone surface; no limestone outcropping through the soil mantle within 300 m of profile described	
Parent material	Probably marine volcanic mud deposited on coral platform before uplift	
Vegetation	Semideciduous (10-15 m) forest with abundant leguminous species	
Climate	Subhumid tropical, MAR about 1 200 mm, MAT 25°C	

Profile description [1]

Ah 0-8 cm Very dark reddish brown (10R 2/2 wet, 2.5YR 3/3 wet crushed) clay; friable to firm moist, slightly hard dry; moderately sticky and moderately plastic wet; very strongly developed very fine angular and subangular blocky structure, breaking to granules; considerable insect aggregations; porous in the mass but peds have only very fine pores; very abundant roots; boundary distinct.

AB 8-25 cm Very dark to dark reddish brown (10R 2/2-3/2 wet, 10R 3/3 wet crushed) clay; slightly more firm than last horizon; rather hard dry; moderately sticky and very strongly plastic wet; weakly developed coarse subangular blocky structure breaking to fine and very fine angular blocks, and coarse granules; porous in the mass but individual peds with only very fine pores; faint indications of clayskins; many roots; boundary merging.

Bt1 25-78 cm Dark red (10R 3/4 slightly moist, 2.5YR 3/6 slightly moist and crushed) clay; firm moist, hard dry; moderately sticky and very strongly plastic wet; very hard to dig at all moisture conditions, compact; strongly developed very coarse angular blocky structure (almost prismatic), breaking to weakly developed medium, fine and very fine angular blocks and coarse granules; moderate to strong development of clayskins on all peds and in root channels; some pressure faces under the lens; few fine roots but large roots common in structural fissures; boundary merging.

Bt2 78-105 cm Red (10R 4/8 dry, 10R 3/6 wet, 2.5YR 4/8 dry crushed) clay; very firm moist, very hard dry; moderately to strongly sticky and very strongly plastic wet; compact and very hard to dig at all moisture conditions; very strongly developed very coarse prismo-blocky structure, breaking to weakly developed fine and very fine angular blocks and coarse granules; very strong development of clayskins and some pressure faces; few very fine pores in peds; occasional (very large) roots; boundary merging.

C 105-140 cm Dark red (10R 3/6 to 7.5R 3/4 moist) clay; firm to friable moist, slightly hard dry; moderately sticky and moderately compact, easier to dig than last horizon (almost loose at contact with underlying limestone); moderately developed medium, fine and very fine angular blocky structure breaking to coarse granules; slightly porous in the mass; very few roots; no recognizable clayskins or pressure faces; boundary sharp.

R 140+ Very hard white limestone with " washed " surface.

(No analyses available)

---

[1] Recorded after heavy rain.

GLEYIC SOLONETZ Sg

Unnamed soil	Mexico
Jiménez and Rodríguez, 1971	
Location	Texcoco-El Peñon road (km 10), 100 m N of road, 19°30'N, 98°57'W
Altitude	2 242 m
Physiography	Lacustrine plain
Parent material	Alluvial deposits from igneous rocks and volcanic ashes
Vegetation	Bare soil with small areas of *Suaeda nigra*
Climate	Semiarid, mild

Profile description

A   0-20 cm   Very dark greyish brown (10YR 3/2 moist) clay; coarse columnar structure; hard moist; plastic and sticky wet; no HCl reaction; cracks filled with sandy material; no roots; abrupt boundary.

E   20-30 cm   Dark brown (7.5YR 3/2 moist) silt loam; massive; loose moist; nonplastic, non-sticky wet; slight HCl reaction; no roots; clear boundary.

Btn   30-50 cm   Dark reddish brown (2.5YR 3/3 dry) and very dusky red (2.5YR 2/2 moist) loam; coarse prismatic structure; slightly plastic and sticky wet; slight HCl reaction; no roots; abrupt boundary; cracks up to 1 cm wide in lower part.

Cr1   50-75 cm   Pale yellow (2.5Y 7/3 moist) silt loam; structureless; slightly plastic and sticky wet; very slight HCl reaction; no roots; diffuse boundary; watertable at 70 cm; many cracks filled with surface material.

Cr2   75-110 cm   Bluish dark grey (10G 3/1 moist) clay; structureless; slightly sticky and slightly plastic wet; slight HCl reaction; no roots; clear boundary; cracks filled with cemented sandy material.

Cr3   110+   Dark olive grey (2.5GY 3/1 moist) clay loam; structureless; slightly plastic.

Horizon	Depth cm	pH		Cation exchange me %										CaCO₃ %
		H₂O	KCl	CEC	TEB	% BS	Ca	Mg	K	Na	Al	H	
A	0—20	9.95	9.4	26.24						89.9			
E	—30	10.0	9.1	9.63						90.9			
Btn	—50	9.5	9.4	14.97						94.2			
Cr1	—75	9.4	9.3										
Cr2	—110	8.8	9.3	31.33						95.9			
Cr3	—110+	9.6	9.25										

Horizon	Soluble salts		Organic matter				Particle size analysis %						Flocc. index
			% C	% N	C/N	% OM	Stones	Coarse sand	Fine sand	Silt	Clay	Texture	
A			1.46	0.17					25.58	23.34	52.08	clay	
E			2.54	0.05					67.72	13.30	18.78	silt loam	
Btn			1.99	0.04					29.92	43.30	26.78	loam	
Cr1			0.80	0.04									
Cr2			1.27	0.06					28.82	15.64	55.54	clay	
Cr3			2.43	0.14									

VITRIC ANDOSOL Tv

Unnamed soil	Costa Rica

Knox and Maldonado, 1969

Location	Near top of Volcán Irazú, 2.3 km S of middle crater
Altitude	2 900 m
Physiography	Nearly level area (2 percent slope) on narrow ridge between deep narrow valleys near summit of volcano
Parent material	Volcanic ash, layered shower horizons
Vegetation	Pasture, with oaks and other trees
Climate	MAR about 2 000 mm, MAT 9ºC

Profile description[1]

C   0-13 cm   Black (10YR 2/1), dark grey (10YR 4/1 dry) (mixture of colours of individual grains) fine sand; structureless; soft, very friable; nonsticky, nonplastic; many roots in upper part; with thin (1-2 cm) layers of medium sand; lower boundary abrupt and wavy.

2Ah   13-22 cm   Very dark brown (10YR 2/2) loam; weak very fine subangular blocky structure; friable; slightly sticky, slightly plastic; few very fine tubular pores; many clean sand grains; common roots; many dead roots in upper part; lower boundary clear and smooth.

2Bw   22-38 cm   Very dark brown fine sandy loam; structureless; friable; slightly sticky, slightly plastic; few fine tubular pores; most sand grains clean; many roots; lower boundary gradual.

3Bw   38-58 cm   Very dark brown (10YR 2/3) sandy loam (more clay than horizon above); weak very fine subangular blocky structure; friable; slightly sticky, slightly plastic; brittle; many very fine and few fine tubular pores; common clean sand grains; few roots; lower boundary gradual.

4BC   58-75 cm   Very dark brown (10YR 2/3) sandy loam; common flecks of yellowish brown along old root channels; weak very fine subangular blocky structure; friable; slightly sticky, slightly plastic; brittle; common very fine tubular pores; common clean sand grains; few roots; lower boundary clear and wavy.

5C1   75-105 cm   Very dark brown (10YR 2/2) sandy loam, common flecks of yellowish brown along old root channels; structureless; friable; slightly sticky, slightly plastic; brittle; very few fine tubular pores; common clean sand grains; very few roots; intermittent layer of black sand at lower boundary with few pieces of charcoal and chunks of reddish (burned) soil; lower boundary clear and irregular.

6Bw   105-120 cm   Very dark greyish brown (10YR 3/2) fine sandy loam, few flecks of yellowish brown along old root channels; weak, very fine subangular blocky structure; friable; slightly sticky, slightly plastic; few very fine tubular pores; very few roots.

---

[1] Moist soil.

Horizon	Depth cm	pH		Cation exchange me %										CaCO₃ %
		H₂O	CaCl₂	CEC	TEB	% BS	Ca	Mg	K	Na	Al	H		
C	0—13	5.5	5.0	0.8		50	0.1	0.1	0.2					
2Ah	—22	4.5	4.3	13.0		14	0.6	0.7	0.5					
2Bw	—38	5.1	4.7	11.5		7	0.4	0.3	0.1					
3Bw	—58	5.5	5.1	12.0		9	0.6	0.3	0.2					
4BC	—75	5.5	5.1	10.1		7	0.4	0.2	0.1					
5C1	—105	5.6	5.3	3.8		8	0.1	0.1	0.1					
6Bw	—120	5.8	5.5	5.7		7	0.1	0.1	0.2					

Horizon	Soluble salts		Organic matter				Particle size analysis %						Flocc. index
			% C	% N	C/N	% OM	Stones	Coarse sand	Fine sand	Silt	Clay	Texture (field)	
C						1.2			75	21	4	fine sand	
2Ah						17.3			69	29	2	loam	
2Bw						8.4			67	25	8	fine sandy loam	
3Bw						6.5			62	28	10	sandy loam	
4BC						6.2			62	29	9	sandy loam	
5C1						3.9			75	20	5	sandy loam	
6Bw						3.5			65	26	9	fine sandy loam	

VITRIC ANDOSOL Tv

Unnamed soil	Costa Rica
Luzuriaga, 1969	Profile CR67
Location	2 km from Tapesco toward Laguna, approximately 10º13'N, 84º24'W
Altitude	1 600 m
Physiography	Convex slope (10 percent) in mountainous landscape
Parent material	Layered volcanic ash (pumiceous)
Vegetation	Grassland, following forest
Climate	Lower montane, MAR 3 500 mm, MAT 17.5ºC

Profile description

Ah1 0-22 cm Very dark brown (10YR 2/2 moist) or dark greyish brown (10YR 4/2 dry) sandy loam; strong fine granular; slightly sticky, slightly plastic; friable; slightly hard; many fine roots; boundary clear, smooth.

Ah2 22-45 cm Very dark brown (10YR 2/2 moist) or dark brown (10YR 4/3 dry) sandy loam; strong fine granular; slightly plastic, slightly sticky; very friable; slightly hard; many fine roots; boundary abrupt, wavy.

Bw 45-90 cm Dark brown to dark yellowish brown (10YR 4/3-4/4 moist) or yellow brown (10YR 5/3 dry) sandy loam; weak medium subangular blocky; slightly plastic, slightly sticky; friable; slightly hard; becomes yellower when rubbed in hands; frequent fine roots; boundary clear and wavy.

2Ah 90-145 cm Dark brown (10YR 3/3 moist) or brown to dark brown (10YR 4/3 dry) sandy loam; weak medium subangular blocky; slightly sticky, slightly plastic; friable; hard; becomes yellower when rubbed in hands; fine roots; boundary clear and wavy.

2Bw 145-175 cm Dark grey brown and dark brown (10YR 4/2-4/3 moist) or yellowish brown (10YR 5/4 dry) sandy loam; weak medium subangular blocky; slightly sticky, slightly plastic; friable; hard; few fine roots.

Horizon	Depth cm	pH		Cation exchange me %											CaCO₃ %
		H₂O	CaCl₂	CEC	TEB	% BS	Ca	Mg	K	Na	Al	H	
Ah1	0—22	5.5	5.0	47		14	4.2	1.7	0.9				
Ah2	—45	5.9	5.2	44		21	6.0	1.7	1.5				
Bw	—90	6.3	5.4	43		15	4.8	0.9	0.7				
2Ah	—145	6.6	5.4	48		22	8.2	1.3	1.0				
2Bw	—175	6.3	5.6	39		25	8.2	1.3	0.3				

Horizon	Soluble salts		Organic matter				Particle size analysis %							Flocc. index
			% C	% N	C/N	% OM	Stones	Coarse sand	Fine sand	Silt	Clay	Texture	
Ah1				1.0	9	15.9		20	12	38	30	clay loam	
Ah2				0.4	7	4.1		25	5	52	18	silt loam	
Bw				0.3	8	3.7		26	14	44	16	sandy loam	
2Ah				0.3	9	3.8		22	10	56	12	silt loam	
2Bw				0.1	4	0.6		47	7	32	14	sandy loam	

MOLLIC ANDOSOL   Tm

Santa Ana series	El Salvador
Bourne, 1963	
Location	Approximately 7 km N of Santa Elena, Usulután
Altitude	560 m
Physiography	Steep slope of volcanic cone
Parent material	Volcanic ash
Vegetation	Coffee plantation

Profile description

Ah   0-30 cm   Dark brown (10YR 3/3 dry) and very dark brown (10YR 2/3 moist) loam; moderate fine and medium granular; diffuse boundary.

AC   30-60 cm   Dark yellowish brown (10YR 4/6 dry) and dark brown (7.5YR 3/4 moist) loam; moderate fine and medium granular; diffuse boundary.

C   60-100 cm   Strong brown (7.5YR 4/6 dry) and dark reddish brown (5YR 3/4 moist) loam; subangular blocky structure very fine to very coarse in size; few faint clayskins in pores; clear boundary.

2B   100-180 cm   Strong brown (7.5YR 4/6 dry) and dark yellowish brown (10YR 3.5/4 moist) loam; subangular blocky structure very fine to very coarse in size; frequent moderately thick clayskins in pores; friable; not sticky; gradual boundary.

2C   180-280 cm   Yellowish brown (10YR 5/4 dry) and yellowish red (5YR 3/6 moist) sandy loam; friable; not sticky; few faint clayskins in pores.

(No analyses available)

PELLIC VERTISOL	Vp

Chac-choben clay	Mexico
Wright and Ruben Lopez, 1968	
Location	Irrigation scheme settlement, Chac-choben, Quintana Roo Territory
Altitude	25 m
Physiography	Flat plain with gilgai microrelief
Parent material	Soft chalky limestone
Vegetation	Semideciduous lowland forest with abundant Orbigyua palms
Climate	Subhumid, tropical, moderately dry season of 2-3 months, MAR about 1 100 mm, MAT about 25°C

Profile description

A   **0-15 cm**
Black (10YR 1/1 moist) clay; generally friable moist but with slightly firm peds, very hard peds dry; moderately sticky and very strongly plastic wet; moderately developed medium and fine blocky structure (mostly angular) breaking to finer angular blocks and granules; abundant roots; no reaction with dilute hydrochloric acid; boundary indistinct.

AB   **15-40 cm**
Brownish black (10YR 3/1 moist) clay; moderately developed medium and fine mainly angular blocky structure breaking to finer angular blocks; firm moist, very hard dry; very sticky and very strongly plastic wet; pressure faces present, but no definite clayskins or slickensides; no reaction with HCl; abundant roots; boundary fairly distinct.

BW   **40-60 cm**
Brownish grey (between 10YR 4/1 and 7.5YR 4/1 moist) clay; somewhat friable moist, firm dry; very sticky and strongly plastic wet; moderate to strong medium and fine angular blocky structure breaking to fine and very fine angular blocks; local reaction with HCl; abundant roots; pressure faces common; indications of slickensides; very weak and intermittent clayskins on peds (not easily seen owing to pressure faces on peds); many fine fragments or concentrations of free carbonates showing as white speckling; boundary distinct.

BC   **60-70 cm**
Brownish and reddish grey (10YR 4/1 dry and 2.5YR 4/1 moist) clay; very sticky and plastic wet; strongly developed fine angular blocky structure (with weak laminar cleavage) breaking to very fine angular blocks and coarse granules (flattened horizontally); pressure faces but few clayskins or slickensides; some general reaction to HCl; abundant roots; some soft, dark brown, fine rounded manganese concretions; boundary merging.

C1   **70-90 cm**
Greyish yellow-brown (10YR 6/2 moist-wet) clay; very friable moist; very sticky and plastic wet; moderate medium angular blocky structure breaking to very fine and fine angular blocks and granules; weak general reaction to HCl; some pressure faces and very occasional very fine rounded manganese concretions; abundant roots; boundary diffuse.

C2   **90-100 cm**
Dark yellowish orange (10YR 6/4 very moist to wet) clay, finely mottled reddish and very dark grey; mottles common very fine, distinct and with clear limits; fine, slightly hard, rounded and subangular manganese nodules with roughened surfaces also common; very sticky and very strongly plastic wet (normal condition of this horizon); many fine fragments of calcium carbonate, probably derived from underlying limestone; strong general reaction with HCl; abundant roots; boundary abrupt.

R   **100+**
Lithified limestone with occasional fissures.

(No analyses available)

EUTRIC PLANOSOL	We
Unnamed soil	Honduras
Simmons and Smyth, 1963	
Location	4 km SSW of town of Choluteca on road to La Trinidad, Choluteca
Altitude	30 m
Physiography	Flattish low coastal terrace system
Parent material	Marine alluvium
Vegetation	Xerophytic woodland with pasture

Profile description

Ah   0-10 cm   Greyish brown (10YR 5/2 dry) mottled with rust brown, loamy sand; weak granular structure; hard in place, loose when removed; gradual contact; pH 6.0.

E   10-25 cm   Light grey (10YR 7/2 dry) mottled with rust brown, loamy sand; structureless; hard and compact but nonsticky and nonplastic; sharp contact; in places a thin layer of gravel between horizon E and horizon Btg1; these horizons are relatively impermeable, and even after water has stood on surface more than 25 hours dry soil may occur at 15 cm depth; pH 5.5.

Btg1   25-50 cm   Dark greyish brown (2.5YR 4/2 dry) sandy clay, mottled with rust brown, some small gravel; coarse blocky structure (weak columnar); some clayskins but not prominent; faces of aggregates grey, centres mottled with rust brown; very hard dry; large cracks form but when breaking a dry clod it does not break along structure faces; sticky and plastic wet.

Btg2   50-65 cm   Similar to layer Btg1 but perhaps browner, more sand, structure less well developed; some slickensides; pH 6.5.

(No analyses available)

LUVIC XEROSOL   X1

Unnamed soil	Mexico
Gile and Hawley, 1968	
Location	Bustillos basin, about 10 km N of Highway 16 on west side of Highway 26 about 11 km WNW of Cuauhtémoc
Altitude	About 2 200 m
Physiography	Broad piedmont slope midway between the Sierra Malpaso and floor of the Bustillos basin; gently undulating surface probably formed by coalescence of alluvial fans
Parent material	Superficial layer of sandy loam (38 cm) overlying 76 cm of slightly gravelly loamy sediments, grading into pebbly and cobbly regolithic gravels
Climate	MAR about 400 mm

Profile description

C	0-38 cm	Light brownish grey (10YR 6/2 dry) or dark greyish brown (10YR 4/2 moist) fine sandy loam; fine stratifications lacking; weak development of a prismatic structure; noncalcareous; abrupt smooth boundary to underlying buried soil.
2Ah1	38-56 cm	Dark greyish brown (10YR 4.5/2 dry) or dark brown (10YR 3/3 moist) heavy fine sandy loam; massive; friable; few roots; few very fine tubular and interstitial pores; noncalcareous; clear smooth boundary.
2Ah2	56-76 cm	Dark greyish brown (10YR 4.5/2 dry) or very dark greyish brown (10YR 3/2 moist) loam; massive to weak medium subangular blocky; friable to firm; few roots; few very fine tubular and interstitial pores; a few fine pebbles with reddish brown staining; noncalcareous; clear boundary.
2BA	76-99 cm	Light brown (7.5YR 5.5/4 dry) or dark brown (7.5YR 3.5/4 moist) heavy sandy loam; weak coarse prismatic; massive internally; friable; no roots; common fine and very fine interstitial pores; sand grains and pebbles thinly stained with clay; noncalcareous; clear boundary.
2Bt	99-114 cm	Light brown (7.5YR 5.5/4 dry) or dark brown (7.5YR 3.5/4 moist) light sandy clay loam; weak coarse prismatic, massive internally; friable to firm; few very fine tubular and interstitial pores; sand grains and pebbles thinly stained with clay; noncalcareous; clear wavy boundary.
2C1	114-130 cm	Brown (10YR 5.5/3 dry) or dark brown (10YR 4/3 moist) very gravelly heavy sandy clay loam; massive; friable; no roots; common fine tubular and interstitial pores; some pebbles have discontinuous black stains; noncalcareous; clear wavy boundary.
2C2	130-163 cm	Dominantly light brown (7.5YR 6/4 dry) or brown (7.5YR 5/4 moist) with some light grey (10YR 8/1, 10YR 7/2 dry) or greyish brown (10YR 5/2 moist) or grey (10YR 5/1 moist) very gravelly sandy clay loam; very firm in place; friable and firm when removed; no roots; fine earth tightly packed in interstices between pebbles; occasional black stainings and fillings; noncalcareous.

(No analyses available)

LUVIC YERMOSOL Yl

Unnamed soil	Mexico
Gile and Hawley, 1968	
Location	About 7 km N of km 1 705 post on Pan-American Highway and 1.6 km E of Highway 45 on EW branch road (Rancho 1 y 2)
Physiography	Lower piedmont slope at extreme south end of Encinillas basin; part of broad coalescent fan surface, in places the site of some recent sedimentation
Altitude	About 1 730 m
Parent material	Possibly a recent alluvial deposit (gravelly loam to clay loam) on old geomorphic surface of mainly rhyolitic gravels
Vegetation	Blue grass, catclaw and mesquite
Climate	MAR about 300 mm

Profile description

A 0-8 cm Reddish brown (5YR 5/4 dry, 5YR 3.5/4 moist) sandy loam; massive; friable; roots common; sand grains and pebbles weakly stained with reddish clay; noncalcareous; clear smooth boundary.

BA1 8-30 cm Reddish brown (5YR 5/4 dry, 5YR 3.5/4 moist) heavy sandy loam; massive; friable to firm; few roots; sand grains and pebbles thinly coated with clay; noncalcareous; clear wavy boundary.

BA2 30-51 cm Reddish brown (5YR 5/4 dry, 5YR 3.5/4 moist) heavy sandy loam; massive; friable to firm; few roots; sand grains and pebbles thinly coated with clay; noncalcareous; clear wavy boundary.

Bt 51-84 cm Reddish brown (5YR 5/4 dry, 5YR 4/4 moist) and red (2.5YR 4/6 dry, 2.5YR 3.5/6 moist) gravelly heavy sandy clay loam, in places with less gravel; moderate medium subangular blocky; firm; few roots; 2.5YR colours (in intricate pattern with 5YR material) occur as irregular veins one to a few millimetres in diameter that mark the most prominent accumulations of clay; sand grains and pebbles prominently coated with clay; weak and moderate medium prismatic in low gravel zones; prism faces have dark stainings and smooth surfaces but no apparent clayskin; noncalcareous; clear wavy boundary.

BC 84-122 cm Dominantly reddish brown (5YR 5/4 dry, 5YR 4/4 moist) with some parts 2.5YR hue, very gravelly light sandy clay loam; massive; friable; few roots; clayey coatings on pebbles and sand grains; thin discontinuous carbonate coatings on some pebbles; fine earth effervesces weakly or is noncalcareous; clear wavy boundary.

C 122-160 cm Reddish brown (5YR 5/4 dry, 5YR 4/4 moist) very gravelly sandy loam; massive; friable; some pebbles have reddish brown clayey coatings; no roots; generally noncalcareous, with a few spots of weak effervescence.

(No analyses available)